M000082855

Gelin

Molecular Modeling
of Polymer Structures
and Properties

Bruce R. Gelin

Molecular Modeling of Polymer Structures and Properties

Hanser Publishers, Munich Vienna New York

Hanser/Gardner Publications, Inc., Cincinnati

The Author:
Bruce R. Gelin, Custom Research and Consulting, 105–4 Trowbridge Street, Cambridge, MA 02138, USA

Distributed in the USA and in Canada by
Hanser/Gardner Publications, Inc.
6600 Clough Pike, Cincinnati, Ohio 45244-4090, USA
Fax: +1 (513) 527-8950

Distributed in all other countries by
Carl Hanser Verlag
Postfach 86 04 20, 81631 München, Germany
Fax: +49 (89) 98 48 09

The use of general descriptive names, trademarks, etc., in this publication, even if the former are not especially identified, is not to be taken as a sign that such names, as understood by the Trade Marks and Merchandise Marks Act, may accordingly be used freely by anyone.

While the advice and information in this book are believed to be true and accurate at the date of going to press, neither the authors nor the editors nor the publisher can accept any legal responsibility for any errors or omissions that may be made. The publisher makes no warranty, express or implied, with respect to the material contained herein.

Library of Congress Cataloging-in-Publication Data
Gelin, Bruce R.
  Molecular modeling of polymer structures and properties / Bruce R.
Gelin.
    p. cm.
  Includes bibliographical references and index.
  ISBN 1-56990-125-2
  1. Polymers—Data processing. 2. Molecular structure—Data
processing. I. Title.
QD381.9.E4G45   1994
547.7′01′1—dc20   93-48573

Die Deutsche Bibliothek - CIP-Einheitsaufnahme
Gelin, Bruce R.:
Molecular modeling of polymer structures and properties /
Bruce R. Gelin. - Munich ; Vienna ; New York : Hanser ;
Cincinnati : Hanser/Gardner Publ., 1994
  ISBN 3-446-16553-3

All rights reserved. No part of this book may be reproduced or transmitted in any form or by any means, electronic or mechanical, including photocopying or by any information storage and retrieval system, without permission in writing from the publisher.

© Carl Hanser Verlag, Munich Vienna New York, 1994
Typeset in Great Britain by Techset Composition Ltd., Salisbury
Printed and bound in Italy by Editoriale Bortolazzi-Stei, s.r.l., Verona

Preface

While new theoretical and analytical methods are always sought after, their reduction to practice is often difficult, and a considerable space of time elapses before the new techniques are brought into widespread use. This has been especially true of the integration of computers into chemical research. This book concentrates on the topic of detailed atomistic modeling of polymer molecules and materials, with the goal of making this aspect of computer-aided chemical research more accessible to the large audience of polymer scientists.

A very considerable history of such molecular modeling already exists in other fields, most notably in bio/pharmaceutical applications. Small molecule modeling dates back to the 1960s, and major advances in protein modeling followed. The first calculation of the molecular dynamics of a protein was done in 1977, and shortly thereafter, the increasing availability of superminicomputers gave research departments a tremendous boost in their ability to pursue computational modeling. Now, the constant improvement in computing capabilities at all levels—personal computers, graphics workstations, and supercomputers—makes it possible for many individuals to have at their disposal levels of computational power unheard of a decade ago. The combination of experience in bio/pharmaceutical modeling and availability of powerful computers makes this an appropriate time to consider applying molecular simulation methods in other fields such as polymers and materials.

Many more chemists and scientists in other fields would use molecular modeling if it were less of a mystery to them. The goal of this book is to explore the application of molecular modeling to a particular field, namely polymer structures and properties. Detailed, atomistic modeling of polymers is not new; one of the first major simulations of the structure of an amorphous, glassy polymer was published in 1985 (see Ref. 64 in Sec. 4.4.3). Even this study of a static, equilibrium structure involved many points of modeling technique and significant computer resources. The scientist wishing to make a theoretical approach to more advanced problems such as thermal behavior and various physical properties might well be discouraged and dismiss the whole subject as hopelessly complex. Further, the scientist may be unsure of the applicability of the models, the computational requirements of the methods, and the quality of the results. Couple this with the less-than-friendly computing environment which is still all too prevalent, and it is not hard to see why polymer modeling is still generally regarded as the province of experts. This need not continue.

This book intentionally avoids questions of computer operations and programming. Computers and their operating systems change too rapidly, and are best covered by the manufacturer's documentation for each type of machine and operating environment. As for programming, it is increasingly the case that scientists do not write their own programs—rather they work with large software packages prepared by others, including commercial organizations—and thus do not want nor need to become involved in software development. On the other hand, enthusiastic claims and marketing literature from the software developers sometimes makes it difficult for the scientist to know what to expect in terms of models, methods, and results. What the scientist needs to understand, and what this book covers, are the *models* and the *computational approaches* that are used to study different problems. Both of these, too, will be improved upon constantly as more scientists and companies pursue theoretical studies, but the basics covered here will always remain fundamental to an understanding of simulation approaches.

The method of this book is to explain the techniques in a general way first, followed by accounts of applications to certain areas. A number of simulations recently reported in the literature are used to illustrate the applications in Chapters 4 through 8. The first three chapters present the general idea of modeling as a simplification process, the development and classification of empirical force fields, and how they are applied to perform various basic calculations such as energy minimization and molecular dynamics. Chapter 3 uses a small molecule as an example to make the details of the energy function explicit. Chapter 4 is devoted entirely to the question of model building, since this is not simple for polymer systems, and has consequences for all further computations. Unlike small-molecule or protein modeling, where it is relatively easy to construct a trial molecular geometry or to use an X-ray crystal structure, polymeric systems do not consist of multiple copies of one prototypical molecule; rather there is a distribution of chain lengths, compositions, and conformations. The polymer model-building process itself can involve significant computations.

Chapter 5 concentrates on the characterization of polymer structure, as revealed by model-building and the simulations which follow. In Chapter 6 the deformation of the equilibrium structures is considered. Considerable information about deformation mechanisms is learned even from simple models of single polymer chains. This serves as a preface to simulations with more complex models. The subject of Chapter 7 is diffusion of small penetrants (e.g., gas molecules) within polymeric materials; related phenomena touched on include characterization of polymer surfaces as regards wetting, coatings, and interdiffusion across polymer-polymer interfaces, and the dynamics of energy transfer within polymers. Chapter 8 shows how mechanical models can be useful in the explanation of polymer electrical properties.

Aside from the necessary characterization of force fields and their operations, this book avoids mathematical treatments in favor of qualitative descriptions of the models and results. Ample mathematical background is available in the references, which are also recommended to those wishing to study the simulation methods in greater detail. This orientation reflects the goal of this book to make polymer modeling more accessible to scientists who may have been discouraged in the past by the apparent exclusion of the field to all but experts.

Computational polymer modeling is currently in a state of rapid development, and what is presented here as the start of the art is likely to be revised and superseded before long. This book attempts to bring the reader to the point from which independent study and evaluation of the current literature are possible. If the book encourages scientists to approach molecular modeling with a critical understanding and realistic expectations, it will have served its purpose.

Bruce R. Gelin

In memoriam Victor M. Gelin (1909–1992)

Contents

Chapter 1
Introduction to Molecular Modeling
1

Chapter 2
Force Fields Based on Empirical Energy Functions
17

Chapter 3
Calculations with Force Fields
35

Chapter 4
Building Models of Polymeric Systems
59

Chapter 5
Modeling of Polymer Structures
80

Chapter 6
Simulation of Mechanical Properties
104

Chapter 7
Diffusion, Surface Phenomena, and Energy Transfer
120

Chapter 8
Electrical Properties of Polymers
144

References
159

Index
167

1

Introduction to Molecular Modeling

The purposes of this chapter are to provide a rationale for the use of modeling as a way of estimating polymer structures and properties, and to acquaint the reader with the spectrum of modeling methods available. We begin with a general discussion of modeling as a means of *structure-based design* of molecules. We differentiate between molecular properties and bulk properties, and discuss the role of rational design in the research process. The second part of this chapter considers the various levels of abstraction used in deriving models, and provides our first general view of the hierarchy of computing methods available.

1.1   Purpose of Modeling

Polymer research, like other basic scientific research, is complicated and expensive. Advances in instrumentation, methodology, and theory are always sought after, both for their fundamental scientific value and for their "economic" value, that is, for their ability to make research proceed more efficiently and effectively. The final goal of this research is to develop new materials, processes, products, and applications.

Experiments to learn the details of polymer structure, to measure polymer properties, and to try to establish relationships between the two, can be very time-consuming and expensive. The synthesis of a new polymeric material in laboratory quantities can require weeks of work by highly skilled scientists and technicians, while tying up expensive equipment and using scarce chemicals and catalysts. The analytical laboratory work needed to characterize the newly synthe-sized material is also expensive to obtain: property measurements vary greatly in complexity, but the total cost of the work, including sample preparation, set-up time of equipment and apparatus, the actual analytical procedure, and sample tracking and reporting, rapidly mounts into many thousands of dollars.

Given these considerations, it is worth investigating methods for property *prediction*. Even if not perfectly accurate, such methods could reasonably indicate whether it might be worthwhile to synthesize the material and do the analytical work; they could also suggest alternative structures to consider. Additional value can accrue from integrating theoretical calculations with experimental programs. As results from both approaches are compared, insights into the structural and mechanistic basis of phenomena can contribute to better understanding of the material under development, and again suggest new formulations or treatments to improve its properties.

1.1.1   Goals of Predictive Methods

One aim of theoretical methods is to develop standardized procedures to compute structures and properties without synthesizing the actual material. That is, we wish to be able to start with an atomic-level model of a proposed polymer and use appropriate theory and calculations to predict its structural details and its material properties, and to use *design at the molecular level* to create a material with the desired properties [1].

This is a rational approach that has been carried out in some cases. For small molecules isolated in space, highly accurate theories which consider the detailed electronic structure are capable of producing the correct geometry and a number of properties of the molecule. If the molecule is flexible and has several geometric isomers, such theories can predict energy differences between the various states and thus tell which one is the most stable isomer. Energy barriers to transitions between states can also be calculated, permitting accurate estimates of the mix of populations and rates of interconversion at room temperature or any other temperature.

1.1.2   Molecular vs Bulk Properties

For some applications, the consideration of a single molecule surrounded by vacuum is a sufficient theoretical model to obtain the properties of interest. For example, the conformational properties, the heat of formation and other thermodynamic properties, the dipole moment, the polarizability and higher electrical moments, the steric and electrostatic fields, and the spectral properties of the molecule can be directly calculated (Fig. 1.1). Significant research effort is directed toward the perfection of methods for these tasks and their extension to new molecular systems.

In other cases, however, it is not solely the properties of one molecule that determine the behavior of interest. In the design of new drugs, for example, the drug molecule interacts with other molecules to trigger what may be a very complicated scheme of reactions and biochemical processes. It may be possible in some cases (or it may be necessary, when there is no information about the molecules with which the drug interacts) to develop improved drugs simply by considering the drug molecule or a series of similar molecules and attempting to correlate the desired activity with chemical structural features. But if structural information exists about the molecules with which the drug interacts, it may be very advantageous to use this information as part of the detailed molecular model of the drug's activity [2].

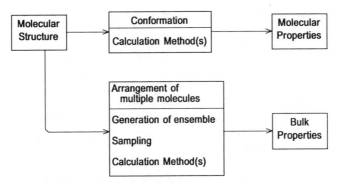

Figure 1.1. Computation of molecular and material properties.

In materials contexts, we are interested in the bulk properties produced by a large collection of molecules, because such properties are the basis of the economic value of the material. The bulk sample may consist of many identical copies of a single molecule, and these may be well ordered as in a crystal, or randomly ordered, as in a fluid or glass; see Fig. 1.2. The sample might also consist of mixtures of several or many different molecules. In the case of long chain molecules, the individual chains may be ordered as in a crystalline domain of an oriented polymer, or they may be very randomly intertwined to form a complicated amorphous network. Further, polymerization conditions usually produce a variety of molecular weights, tacticity, and main-chain branching patterns; these in turn affect how the molecules occupy space and thus what density, permeability, mechanical attributes, and other properties the bulk material will possess. In all of these cases, it is clear that the properties we want to predict must depend on the molecular properties of the component molecules, but the dependence is complex and also involves the arrangement of the molecules. The challenge is to calculate both the individual-chain properties and the bulk material properties.

Figure 1.2. Regularity and order in matter. Some materials consist of many identical copies of one molecule, well ordered as in a crystal (a), or in random relative arrangement as in a gas or fluid (b). Other materials consist of non-identical molecules, with some domains exhibiting a high degree of local order and others disordered (c).

1.1.3   Rational Design of Molecules and Substances

The interaction of molecular-level theory with experimental work in materials research takes two forms that have already been mentioned (see Fig. 1.3). One approach is to think of theory as an initiator in discovery research. In this point of view, the purpose of calculations is to evaluate materials that have not been created, with the goal of distinguishing the most productive possibilities from those which will not have the desired properties. The other approach is to consider theoretical work as part of an integrated program of theory and experiment. Here it is hoped that by providing a structural basis for the interpretation of phenomena, theory will help introduce a rational means for designing new materials. Simultaneously, each experiment serves as a check on theoretical predictions, and it is hoped that the two approaches will complement and strengthen each other.

Such structure-directed design has come to be known as *rational design*. Its proponents see applications in a wide range of research activities where the goals are reached by creation of new molecules and materials. These include at least the following fields: pharmaceuticals, agricultural chemicals, food and cosmetics, flavors and fragrances, polymeric materials, and inorganic materials such as solid catalysts, metals, and composites. The work is not limited to creation of completely new molecules — it also includes designing novel arrangements or aggregates of existing molecules, as well as interpreting the results of materials processing (orienting, annealing, crystallization, etc.).

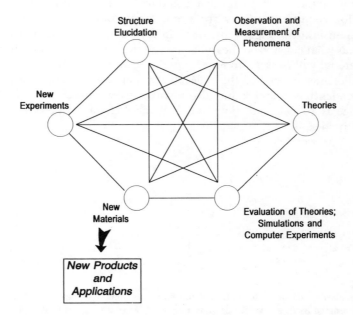

Figure 1.3. The interaction and integration of theory, calculation, and experiment in materials (and other) research.

1.2   Modeling as an Abstraction

Polymer systems are in general highly complex. In all but very specifically synthesized materials, the single chains vary in length (degree of polymerization), the chain compositions may vary in a regular or random fashion, and stereochemical centers along the chains may have regular or random orientations. Furthermore, in real materials many chains are involved, and they are in general not ordered; even in highly crystalline materials, there are usually also amorphous regions. How to treat this mixture of situations and estimate overall properties is a difficult problem. It is not a straightforward process to develop models that include all the material states and interactions present in the sample, and in the proper proportions. Also, models that contain sufficient variety and quantity of local structures may need to be very large and unwieldy.

Accordingly, the first principle of modeling is one of *simplification*, though the degree of simplification varies considerably according to the aspects of polymer structure studied, as discussed later in this chapter.

A dictionary definition of modeling states that it is the act or art of making a copy or imitation of an existing object; implicit is the idea of removing detail and complexity to facilitate concentration on some particular aspect of the object modeled. While the context of this book is computer modeling, it is useful to consider briefly some of the modeling that was done, both in chemistry and other fields, before computers were in widespread use.

1.2.1   Physical Models and Computational Models

A familiar example of modeling in industry is the building of a replica, or a scale model, of a complex manufactured object. For example, exact replicas of cars were built of wood, plaster, or other materials long before the design was committed to manufacturing. In this case, much of the purpose of the model was simply to view it and evaluate the design or aesthetic qualities; a solid model afforded only limited opportunities for making measurements, and evaluating operating characteristics was not possible. In the case of airplanes, scale models were important for wind-tunnel evaluations, a form of operational testing using a model. Nowadays, of course, large and increasing amounts of computer modeling are used in the automobile, aircraft, and many other manufacturing industries.

A somewhat light-hearted but illustrative view of physical modeling is given in Fig. 1.4. The "basic model" shown in the figure is one of the simplest problems in freshman physics, yet it captures much of the reality of the situation. A slightly better model, taking into account sliding friction and wind resistance, is also shown. Another amusing physical model was created from mousetraps and ping-pong balls to show how a chain reaction works [3]. An array of mousetraps is placed on the floor of a large room; each trap is cocked and has two ping-pong balls placed on it. To start the chain reaction, one ping-pong ball is tossed into the room. It hits a trap, sending

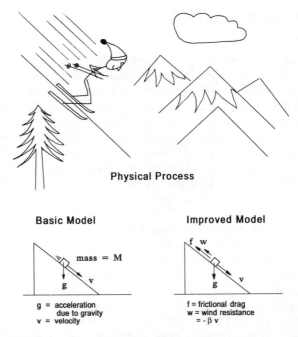

Figure 1.4. Abstraction and simplification make it easier to model physical processes.

its two ping-pong balls into the air; they land on two traps, springing up four balls; and so on. Eventually all the traps have been sprung and the "simulation" comes to an end.

In chemistry, solid models have played a very important role in helping scientists understand the three-dimensional nature and spatial relationships of molecules. The Corey-Pauling-Koltun models [4] are colored solid balls truncated and machined to interlock at the correct angles with the correct scale distances between centers. Numerous chemical researchers relied heavily on these models. One significant example is the Nobel Prize-winning work on molecular complexes by D.J. Cram [5] and others. Even earlier, custom-built models played a major role in Watson and Crick's unraveling of the structure of DNA [6].

But for all their utility, physical models have some disadvantages. Large structures are time-consuming and expensive to build, and they can be difficult to support physically, due to the weight of the model materials. Once such a large model is built, it may be nearly impossible to look inside it to see internal structures of interest. Modification, especially in the interior, could be difficult. While they are accurate representations of molecular structure and geometry, models are incorrect in other respects. They are not flexible, and do not undergo the vibrations that all molecules execute at any temperature. They do not represent nonbonded interactions, such as hydrogen bonds, van der Waals interactions, and electrostatic attractions or repulsions. For these and other reasons, computational models of atoms and molecules are desirable.

In computer modeling of any physical system, we wish to represent the essential physical features of the system, while removing unnecessary detail and complexity. The same process of abstraction was done in Fig. 1.4. What we desire is a model which is:

- mathematically or numerically tractable
- sufficiently physically realistic to be able to represent the phenomena of interest
- easy to set up, define, enter, and revise
- easy to interpret and relate to experimental observations.

These criteria apply to any computer model, whether it represents an automobile crashing into a wall, or less violent shaping and forming of materials; or global weather and climate; or a nuclear fusion apparatus. For an example of modeling in a very different context, the reader is referred to Ref. [7], which describes how assumptions about world economics and resources lead to scenarios about the future. In this book about polymer modeling, we will be concerned with the attributes listed above as they relate to models of polymer chains and networks.

The first characteristic, numerical tractability, is closely related to the computational facilities available, and has been dramatically affected by the continuing evolution of computers. What would have been an intractable or extremely computationally intensive model three decades ago can now be conveniently evaluated on inexpensive desktop computers. The effects of supercomputers and their increased availability to many researchers will continue to redefine the levels of complexity that researchers will routinely use. Nevertheless, chemical theory is sufficiently complicated that accurate calculations even for small to medium molecules make great demands on today's fastest computers, and simplifications are required. In Chapter 2 we discuss the simplified models of molecular forces and interaction that are used in this book, and in Chapter 3 we show their operations and techniques. Chapter 4 goes in detail into the process of building up polymer structures from basic units and introducing the characteristics that give polymeric materials their important properties. The rest of the book is about applications and results.

While the goal of model-building is simplification, it must not simplify the relevant phenomena out of existence. For example, as we shall see soon, much modeling represents molecules as collections of classical particles connected by various sorts of restraining forces (i.e., "balls and springs" — although, as we shall also see, this terminology is actually inappropriate). In such models, the electrons which are responsible for the bonding and other interatomic forces are not explicitly represented; they are accounted for in some time-averaged or steady-state fashion. Therefore models of this type cannot directly account for phenomena that are electronic in nature, such as UV/visible absorption spectra or electrical conductivity. Models must be appropriate to the effects under study. Most of the phenomena covered in this book are susceptible to good description without taking electronic degrees of freedom into account; rather, it is the overall folding and resistance to reshaping of the covalent structure that governs these properties. This can be well accounted for with models that depend only on the coordinates of the atomic nuclei (actually, the atoms, considered as point masses). Even in Chapter 8, which discusses the modeling of electrical phenomena in polymers, much can be learned simply by considering the balance of forces arising from electronic and covalent effects, and the response of the covalent structure to average forces arising from interactions of charged groups with external electromagnetic fields.

The ease of setting up, defining, entering, and revising models also bears a strong dependence on computer hardware and software advances. How a model is expressed in software will play a major role in whether it is convenient to use and revise. If the conditions of the system can be expressed as parameters that are easily altered by changing a table of numbers, or if structures can be modified directly on a graphics screen, the model will be easier to change and apply to a wider variety of problems. As we shall see, some aspects of polymer model building have been fully automated, while others are not straightforward and require considerable computational effort; this is the subject of Chapter 4.

Finally, the ease with which a model can be interpreted and compared with experimental data and phenomena is critical to its success. One requirement is a set of convenient procedures for the numerical evaluation of various properties from the model, under correct conditions and with valid sampling; another aspect is the interpretation of qualitative phenomena. For example, it may be a straightforward operation to request the average kinetic energy per atom in a dynamical model of a polymer, but to evaluate whether the sample has undergone melting may require a detailed analysis of the internal motions and the persistence or loss of order. Throughout Chapters 4–8, we will cite work in which modeling results are compared with whatever experimental information is known, and best attempts are made to reconcile the results of theoretical simulations and experiment.

1.2.2   Qualitative and Quantitative Applications

Modeling studies are undertaken to answer both qualitative and quantitative questions. Quantitative studies seek to determine a numerical value for some property, or a range of values over a domain of conditions. Qualitative studies have as their purpose the elucidation of a mechanism or explanation of factors involved in a phenomenon. Some models may be capable of producing both types of results, but may be evaluated only for one or the other purpose in a given study. Other approaches may provide only qualitative accounts of behavior; still others may give useful numerical estimates, but without explaining the atomic-level interactions that lead to the qualitative behavior of a realistic system.

A detailed molecular model which represents atoms interacting by forces of a "chemical" nature — which we will define more precisely in Chapter 2, but which include bond stretching, bond angle bending, and so on — can be evaluated for both qualitative and quantitative purposes. We may want to know whether the addition of a functional group to a monomer makes a stiffer or more flexible material, without the necessity of computing quantitative estimates of the stiffness. Similarly, one could

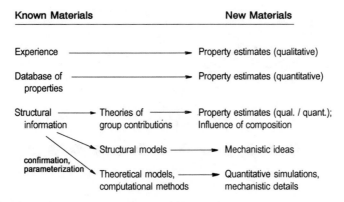

Figure 1.5. Qualitative and quantitative modeling approaches.

evaluate the effects of composition on chain packing in a crystalline domain, or the relative amounts of unoccupied space in polymers of various compositions at various temperatures. See the schematic representation in Fig. 1.5.

On the other hand, there are many properties for which one would like to have numerical estimates. These range from simple physical factors such as density to materials properties such as moduli, yield strength, gas permeability, resistance to burning, or susceptibility to biodegradation. The trend in such studies is to use increasingly realistic models with accurate representations of internal forces to produce simulations that give numerical results.

1.2.3   Atomic and Coarser-Grained Models

The most detailed (and potentially the most accurate) model for evaluation of physical properties of materials would make use of all of our knowledge about the structure of matter. A material sample consisting of an ensemble of molecules would be represented by all the atoms that constitute the molecules; the atoms, in turn, would consist of the nuclei and the electrons. For practical reasons, it is not possible to work with such a model, so recourse must be had to various levels of approximation. Fig. 1.6 depicts a progression of the most commonly used models, starting with the "ultimate" model just mentioned, and showing how detail is removed to arrive at coarser-grained models.

A commonly used level of abstraction is the atomic ball-and-spring model already mentioned (and criticized as a misnomer); we will characterize this model in more detail in Chapter 2. The major simplification is that electronic details are not calculated explicitly, but the role of the electrons is accounted for in terms of the chemical bonding and valence preferences of the atoms and groups. The number of particles in the system is reduced by approximately an order of magnitude; the most common atom, carbon, is treated as a single particle instead of a nucleus with 6

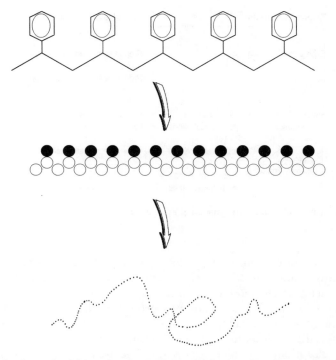

Figure 1.6. Levels of structural approximation in the representation of a polymer chain.

electrons. Moreover, the computational methods are drastically simplified by the elimination of the extensive and time-consuming electronic calculations that make up molecular orbital theory. What remains is a series of evaluations of energy contributions for the deformation of bonds, bond angles, torsions, and nonbonded interactions. The details of these procedures are the subject of Chapters 2 and 3.

To reduce the number of particles (and hence the magnitude of the calculation) further, some approaches have used so-called united atoms, in which hydrogens are treated together with the heavier atom to which they are attached. Thus a methyl group, $-CH_3$, is a single particle whose van der Waals radius and mass are adjusted to take account of the hydrogens. Many unified atoms can be defined to handle all chemical situations present in a system, and the number of particles can thus be reduced by another factor of 2 to 3; for example, polyethylene simplifies from $[-CH_2-]_n$ to $[-M-]_n$, where M represents the methylene group $-CH_2-$; the number of particles in each chain is reduced to one-third of the original number. In other polymers that contain polar hydrogens (e.g., attached to heteroatoms such as nitrogen), this simplification can be applied to all hydrogens, or only to the non-polar ones that do not have the potential of forming hydrogen bonds.

In coarser-grained models, successively larger units may be reduced to a single element. One widely used model is the Rouse model [8], in which each monomer is reduced to a "bead," and the beads are connected by rigid rods. Classical springs with Hooke's Law restraining forces may be substituted for the rigid rods, as in the Rouse-Zimm model [9]. The rods may be constrained so that successive bonds form standard valence angles, or they may be unconstrained [10]. In the case of polyethylene, the united-atom model is the same as the bead model; however, as is introduced in the next Chapter, the force components employed in most force fields have more terms than just the bond stretch (the "spring" part of the ball-and-spring model) and the bond-angle bend.

At this point it is also appropriate to mention lattice models (Fig. 1.7). In these models particles are constrained to points of a lattice, which may exist in two or three dimensions and may have a variety of geometries (cubic, diamond, etc.). There is no representation of bonds, bond angles, and other "chemical" entities; rather there are rules governing the jumping of any particle from one lattice point to another. Monte Carlo methods provide the means to generate sequences of jumps and eventually the statistical ensembles from which properties are deduced. While there are extensive methodology and literature associated with lattice methods [11], this book concentrates on atomic representation of molecular structure and the methods to evaluate properties from it. It is important, however, to note that lattice methods have been used at least as much as atomistic models thus far in the history of computational polymer modeling. From a modeling point of view, lattice models simplify the physical system by removing the details of chemical valence and concentrating on the particle–particle interactions that produce many of the characteristics of dense systems.

Further structure simplifications introduce rods and other discrete elements to represent whole monomers or even larger portions of molecules. Again this is beyond the scope of this book, in which we are concerned with the dynamics of realistic molecular representations. We will work primarily with all-atom and united-atom models of polymer structure, but on occasion we will refer to results or principles derived from the coarser-grained models.

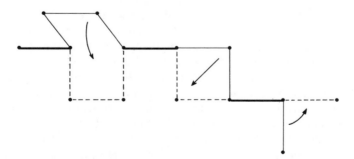

Figure 1.7. In lattice models, particles are constrained to the points of a regular lattice. The system evolves through jumps of one or more particles. The validity of the jumps is decided by an energetic model and/or a rule.

1.2.4   Levels of Computational Approximation

We have alluded above to detailed calculations that treat all the nuclei and electrons in a system, as well as to simpler forms of calculations that can be used. In this section we define these levels in a descriptive manner and specify their ranges of applicability given the present state of computing facilities [12].

1.2.4.1   Ab Initio *Molecular Orbital Calculations*

It has often been said that all of chemistry and molecular structure was solved, in principle, as soon as the Schrödinger equation, which governs the motions of electrons and nuclei in atoms and molecules, was written down [13]. The catch, and the truth, in that statement is in the two words "in principle." Indeed, the Schrödinger equation's applications over decades have proven that it is a correct prescription for computing results of any desired accuracy for any molecular system that does not involve relativistic effects (and these can be treated properly with correction terms). But it cannot be solved analytically for anything larger than a system of one nucleus with one electron around it — the hydrogen atom, the He$^+$ cation, and so on. This is usually illustrated in any introductory quantum mechanics text. It is important to note that these exact orbital forms, while occurring in only a tiny fraction of molecules, are very significant as prototypes out of which the orbitals of more complex systems can be built. Decades of work have been devoted to developing numerical procedures and approximations to obtain reasonably accurate solutions for the molecular Schrödinger equation.

In the most rigorous approach to the problem, calculations are begun with minimal assumptions. The atomic nuclei are positioned by estimation or other means, and the calculation proceeds given only these nuclear coordinates, the number of electrons the system contains, and a set of atomic orbital forms assigned to each atom or type of atom. Because this method makes no other assumptions, it is called the *ab initio* — from the beginning — technique. The calculation produces results in the form of occupancies of the various orbitals, from which the location and order of chemical bonds can be deduced. Such calculations are very numerically intensive and thus time-consuming; depending on the accuracy required and the size of the set of orbitals used, the calculation might take a few minutes to a half-hour of supercomputer time for a small organic molecule consisting of 20 atoms.

In a refinement of this technique, at the end of the calculation cycle of the previous paragraph, the nuclei are shifted by small amounts in directions that should lower the energy of the system. How the nuclear shifts are generated need not concern us here, but the analogous techniques will be fully explained for simpler levels of calculations which are subject of the next chapter. The electronic calculation is completed for the new nuclear positions, the nuclei are shifted again, and so on, until a convergence criterion is reached. This criterion may be the failure of the energy to drop further, the reduction of the coordinate shifts to sufficiently small values, or the reduction in average force on an atom. This process, known as geometry optimization, is obviously even more computer-intensive, as it multiplies the effort of a single calculation by the number of steps needed to reach convergence. Supercomputer time for geometry optimization of the 20-atom organic molecule could be measured in hours if a large set of orbitals is used and the most accurate methods are applied.

We reiterate that these expensive calculations can be made to give results of any desired accuracy, provided we are willing to allocate the necessary computer time. We will not go further into the details of technique here; instead we refer the reader to standard texts and literature (e.g., Ref. [12]). The point, however, is that such calculations provide an anchor point, or a basis for evaluation, of the less exact but more rapidly executed computations that can be widely employed by the majority of researchers.

1.2.4.2 Semiempirical Molecular Orbital Calculations

To reduce the computational requirements of the *ab initio* technique it is necessary to make some simplifications and approximations. This has led to a family of approaches known as *semiempirical* methods, which omit, simplify, or replace the most time-consuming aspects of the *ab initio* calculation. Again we will leave the details to the references, and summarize the major methods.

One of the largest demands for computer resources in the *ab initio* method comes from the need to evaluate a great number of interaction terms. Many of the individual terms are very small, and their contributions may nearly cancel. Completely or partially neglecting these terms produces a great time savings, while still providing reasonably useful results. The corresponding methods, CNDO (for Complete Neglect of Differential Overlap) and INDO (Intermediate Neglect of Differential Overlap), were introduced by Pople and co-workers [14] by 1970 and made possible single-point energy calculations in a few seconds to a few minutes for small organic molecules. A series of other "NDO" methods have followed; one of the early and well-investigated ones is the MNDO [15] method (Modified Intermediate Neglect of Differential Overlap) and several variants, with designations such as MNDO and MNDO/3 (see Clark's book, Ref. [12], for more information, including an exhaustive compendium of molecules and properties to which the MNDO methods have been applied). Still other methods of approximating the calculation have led to a variety of models such as AM1, [16] PM3, [17] etc. Two major program packages, AMPAC and MOPAC, [18] embody a choice of these techniques and have been improved and extended to take advantage of advances in computer hardware. These methods can now be applied to molecules with hundreds of atoms. A recent landmark calculation of the C_{540} fullerene [19] represents an example of the high performance obtainable and the very large systems that have been studied with semiempirical methods.

1.2.4.3 Molecular Mechanics

Simplifying the physical model still more, molecular mechanics methods deal only with the nuclei, whose motion is governed by a "force field" that represents the equilibrium, time-averaged effects of the electrons. The force field is most commonly represented in terms of chemically intuitive entities such as bond stretching/compression, valence angle deformation, torsion or rotation about bonds, and nonbonded interactions. The format and implementation of this approach are developed in the next chapter, and its applications will concern us for the remainder of this book.

The force field approach has the advantage of great speed; the conformational or "strain" energy of the small 20-atom organic molecule can be calculated in a fraction of a second, even on a desktop computer. Very large systems can be treated: these include globular proteins either alone or surrounded by solvent; nucleic acids; and polymeric or inorganic systems consisting of thousands of atoms.

Additionally, the force field approach lends itself to "molecular dynamics," a computational technique in which the motion of the system is calculated as a function of time, given initial assumptions about the distribution of energy in the system [20–23]. Particle trajectories are developed by starting with the initial velocity and forces acting on each particle (atom or united atom), and propagating the system forward in very short time steps. This corresponds to a numerical integration of the Newtonian equations of motion. The process is formally analogous to celestial and planetary mechanics, except that the particles in a molecular system experience a different force field from the 2-body, central gravitational force field that governs planetary motion.

Several recent examples from the literature show the magnitudes of systems that can be simulated using empirical force field models and the molecular dynamics technique. In a study of the thermal denaturation of hen egg-white lysozyme, the model system contained a protein unit surrounded by solvent, for a total of 17,299 atoms; more than 1700 hours of supercomputer time were used [24]. The properties of detergents were studied using a system with three types of particles, a non-polar one representing oil, a polar particle representing water, and a third with both a polar and a nonpolar part, representing the detergent; the total number of particles simulated was 31,735 [25]. A simulation of SiO_2 at various densities in a box 240 Å on a side required 41,472 particles to represent the Si and O atoms; the calculations took 1200 hours on a parallel computer [26].

The disadvantage of force fields is that they are not rigorously derived from first principles, but represent an approximation to the true forces acting in molecules. Much work goes into the choice of functional forms and adjustable parameters that make up force fields, and much controversy surrounds the validity of results. Fortunately, these methods have been very widely applied, and there is a large and growing body of calculational results that can be compared to a variety of experimental data, ranging from conformations and thermodynamic quantities through dynamical phenomena. The more accurate quantum-mechanical methods are also increasingly used to compute such "data" when it is not easily accessible through experiment; this broadens the range of information available to guide force field development. Within certain limits, which continue to expand, the validity of molecular mechanics and dynamics has been well demonstrated [27, 28, 29].

Another disadvantage or limitation of force field methods is that the model on which they are based does not represent the electrons directly, but rather only in terms of their time-averaged effects in creating the molecular forces. This means that these methods cannot be applied to problems which involve electronic phenomena or changes of electronic state, such as chemical reactions. Applications should be further limited to situations in which the deviations from the time-averaged, equilibrium electronic distribution are small. Large deformations of the system, or equivalently, high temperatures, may cause violations of this principle and lead to inaccurate results. One approach that may alleviate these drawbacks is to use a quantum-mechanical calculation for the part of the system where electronic effects are important, while the surrounding "spectator region" is treated with classical mechanics. Several of the widely used empirical force field programs have begun to include such facilities.

1.2.4.4 Integrated Molecular Graphics Systems

It is impossible in the current environment of pervasive and ubiquitous computing technology to omit mention of the modern implementations of the computational modeling methods described here [30]. The trend in commercial software packages [31] is to integrate the computational methods with graphical systems for entering the problem and displaying and analyzing the results. An increasing portion of the manual aspects of structure definition and other bookkeeping has been replaced by these integrated packages. They also make the various simulation packages easier to run by guiding the user through the input and problem specification phases with menu systems, fill-in-the-blank forms, and other ease-of-use aids.

Initially, the attraction of molecular graphics was simply the visualization of results that were formerly disguised in masses of paper output produced by the older software systems. For example, the results of an energy minimization of a large molecule consist of the initial set of atomic coordinates and the final set (or, equivalently, the initial set and a set of atomic shifts that occurred during the minimization). Using these, one could look at the shifts of certain atoms or small groups of atoms, but without visualization it was very difficult to get an overall idea of what took place or where the shifts constituted a significant group motion.

In the context of rational drug design, molecular graphics offered the opportunity to look at the three-dimensional shapes of drugs and receptors, and even to attempt to fit drug molecules interactively into receptor models. This modern setting of the "lock-and-key" model was no doubt useful, but it appears that rational drug design involves much more analytical work in addition to visual fitting, and graphics systems have had to undergo considerable expansion to respond to the new requirements.

In the context of polymer systems, visualization is a relatively new option, whose value may not have been so obvious; in part, this is because molecular-level analysis of polymer structures is also a relatively more recent approach. The procedures and results obtainable from this approach are the subject of this book.

It should be noted that most of the modeling and simulation techniques that are now applied to polymer systems were developed in other contexts (drug design, protein studies, etc.). Accordingly there is much that can be taken from that earlier work, and in many examples we will refer to calculations that have been done for other purposes. It is also appropriate to repeat the caution that this field is in a state of rapid development, so that current techniques are constantly being revised and improved.

1.3   Summary

Computer modeling of physical systems provides a way to carry out analytical studies of the mechanistic details that produce observed phenomena. It is an outgrowth of a general trend toward structure-based chemical research and design, which has also been called rational design. The most accurate computational approaches can be applied only to computation of the molecular properties of small molecules or systems, so approximations are a necessity. Here we have considered those approximations as different levels of abstraction, which progressively neglect more details of the system, and in exchange offer opportunities to study larger systems for longer times. Aside from testing theoretical approximations and providing a means to judge the suitability of different approaches, computer simulations can provide mechanistic insights into how material behavior is related to molecular properties and microscopic details of the arrangement of many molecules.

2

Force Fields Based on
Empirical Energy Functions

As indicated in Chapter 1, there are several levels of approximation with which chemical systems can be modeled. For large systems, or for systems whose time evolution over more than very short periods is to be investigated with molecular dynamics, the only feasible alternative is to use force field methods. In this chapter, we shall define the empirical force field model, specify its general characteristics, and give examples of the functional forms and adjustable parameters involved. This will also permit us to show how different force fields can be classified and compared. In the next chapter, we describe the operations and practicalities of using force fields and show how various calculations are carried out.

2.1   The Energy of a Molecule Expressed as a Function of Its Atomic Coordinates

2.1.1   The Born-Oppenheimer Approximation

The correct description of a chemical system, starting from first principles, is a mathematical formulation which governs the motion of the component parts, the nuclei and the electrons. In the quantum-mechanical description, these components are expressed in terms of the probability of finding a particle at any point in space. The electronic distributions are such that there is an appreciable probability of finding some electrons dispersed over an atomic radius or more. The nuclei, on the other hand, are much heavier and are highly localized. It is valid in all but highly excited states to make a formal separation of the electronic and nuclear motions; then the electronic problem can be solved for a given fixed set of nuclear coordinates. This is the Born-Oppenheimer approximation.

From this approximation it is a short step to the concept of energy functions governing nuclear motion. The concept is simplest if we consider a diatomic molecule whose two nuclei are separated by a distance R. Solving the electronic problem would produce an energy E. As we vary R and repeat the electronic calculation, a curve of E as a function of R would be mapped out. In fact, calculations of this type have

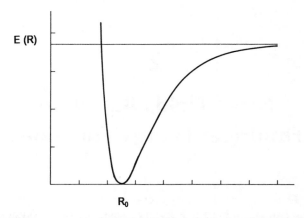

E (R)

R_0

Figure 2.1. The potential energy of the H$_2$ molecule as a function of the internuclear separation R.

been done to very high accuracy (an early example is the computation of the internuclear potential for H_2 by Kolos and Wolniewicz [32, 33, 34], and the curve generated is similar to that of Fig. 2.1. The energy is a minimum at some particular separation $R = R_0$, rises steeply as the nuclei approach more closely, and also rises as the nuclei are pulled apart, but only to a point. At a large enough separation, the energy remains constant regardless of any further increase in internuclear distance, and the molecule may be considered to have dissociated into its component atoms. The energy at "infinite" separation may be taken as the relative zero of energy, in which case bonding energies are negative. In molecular mechanics, the energy at the minimum point on the curve, $E(R_0)$, is taken as the zero, and the (positive) energy at any other point is the so-called strain energy.

The true quantum-mechanical potential curve thus mapped out can be closely approximated by a simple *analytical function* — in this case the Morse function:

$$E(R) = D_0 \{\exp[-A(R - R_0)] - 1\}^2 \tag{2.1}$$

This analytical function is the energy function for the bond stretching or compression of the diatomic molecule. There is nothing intrinsically classical about it — it is simply a convenient approximation to the "true" potential obtained from the accurate electronic calculations. It is an *empirical* energy function in the sense that its adjustable parameters, D_0 and R_0, have been arrived at by fitting externally obtained (in this case, computed) data. In a small range of the separation coordinate near the value where the energy is a minimum (namely $R = R_0$), an even simpler analytical function $K_R(R - R_0)^2$ gives a good approximation to the energy curve; this harmonic approximation is shown in Fig. 2.2.

For polyatomic molecules, the same conceptual program could be carried out to obtain an energy which could be expressed as a function of the atomic Cartesian coordinates of all N atoms in the molecule,

$$E = E(x_i, y_i, z_i) \quad \text{for} \quad i = 1, 2, 3, \ldots, N \tag{2.2}$$

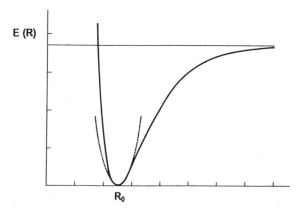

Figure 2.2. The simple harmonic form $K_R (R - R_0)^2$ (dashed curve) is a good approximation to the Morse potential near $R = R_0$.

Alternatively, the energy can be expressed as a function of internal coordinates (such as bond lengths and bond angles) or symmetry coordinates, which are particular combinations of internal coordinates chosen so as to take advantage of molecular symmetry. In any case, a minimal set of $3N - 6$ coordinates (or $3N - 5$ for linear molecules), designated $\{S_i\}$, is required to define the internal geometry of a molecule of N atoms, and the energy can be expressed in terms of these coordinates,

$$E = E(S_i) \quad \text{for} \quad i = 1, 2, 3, \ldots, 3N - 6 \tag{2.3}$$

In the diatomic molecule example above, the data used to parameterize the energy function came from a theoretical calculation. It is also possible to determine the parameters by fitting to experimental data. In fact, historically this was the original method, and because of this reference to observations, the resulting force fields are called *empirical* force fields.

2.1.2   Modeling Nuclear Degrees of Freedom

There have been two major experimental motivations to use empirical energy functions for the modeling of the non-electronic degrees of freedom. One has to do with molecular vibrations, and the other with molecular conformations. Modern force field formulations endeavor to account for both of these attributes as well as additional properties. We discuss the list of properties and data used for force field parameterization in the second part of this chapter. For an account of the historical development of force field approaches, with many early references, see Ref. [35].

The vibrational spectrum of molecules, as observed by infrared, Raman, and other types of spectroscopy, arises from molecular vibrations which occur with no change of the electronic state of the molecule; most typically, it is the vibrational spectrum of the ground electronic state which is observed. Within the Born-Oppenheimer approximation, the nuclei are viewed as executing small oscillations about an equilibrium conformation which is a result of the time-averaged or steady-state electronic configuration. Such a classical view of vibrations lends itself to description in terms of restraining potentials acting on the nuclei, expressed in terms of the internal coordinates S_i introduced above. Just as in classical mechanics, the important elements are the force constants, which are related to the second derivatives of the restraining potentials as expressed in the suitably chosen set of coordinates. In these formulations the molecular geometry is of less interest, as the restraining potentials are set up to produce the experimental geometry or a model geometry made of idealized values; similarly, the emphasis is not on the molecular energy, but on the vibrational spectrum produced by the potentials [36].

An alternative formulation of energy functions arose for a different application, namely that of conformational analysis. The phenomena to be accounted for here are the energy differences of rotational isomers, the heats of formation, and the reactivities of organic molecules. The central concept is the strain energy in a molecule, derived by considering deformations from "normal" or ideal bond lengths, bond angles, and other internal coordinates; this gave rise to the field of conformational analysis [37]. The goal of modern force fields has been increasingly to account for both vibrations and conformations. The idea of using a variety of experimental information to determine a force field that can be applied to predict a similar variety of results is pictured in Fig. 2.3. The term "consistent force field" has been used to describe the fact that the force field is made to be consistent with both (or multiple) types of data [38].

We now turn to a simple and schematic formulation which makes these ideas

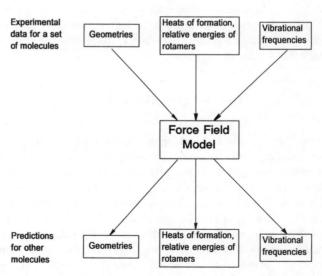

Figure 2.3. A "consistent" force field is derived from several types of molecular information, and can be used to predict similar information for new molecules.

more precise and indicates the role of both force constants and strain energy in empirical energy functions.

2.1.3   Form of the Potential Energy Function

To develop a general empirical energy expression, we begin with a molecular conformation which represents a local or global minimum of the energy, and write the energy expression as a series expansion about this point. Some choices of coordinate systems are described in the second half of this chapter, but for now we will consider the energy to be expressed as a function of a set of generalized coordinates $\{S_i\}$, i.e., $E = E(S_i)$. The Taylor series expansion of the energy for very small deformations S_i is mathematically as follows:

$$E = E_0 + \sum G_i(\Delta S_i) + \sum K_i(\Delta S_i)^2 + \sum F_{ij}(\Delta S_i)(\Delta S_j)$$
$$+ \text{ terms of 3rd order in } (\Delta S_i) + \text{ higher order terms} \tag{2.4}$$

In the first summation, the G_i are the first derivatives with respect to the coordinates, or the gradients of the energy, i.e.,

$$G_i = \partial E/\partial S_i \tag{2.5}$$

But at the minimum, all of these gradients are zero — that is the definition of the minimum of a function — and the energy is the constant E_0, which can be thought of as the "residual" strain energy inherent in the molecule. As we move away from the minimum, these gradients will not in general be zero, and the first sum is a linear approximation to the true rise of the energy as the molecule moves away from its local minimum. This first sum depends on the slope of the molecular potential surface near the local minimum.

The second and third sums are both of second order in the ΔS_i, but they are written separately to emphasize a distinction between the "diagonal" terms — those involving a single coordinate S_i — and the "cross-terms," which explicitly contain deformations for two different coordinates, S_i and S_j, and which represent the coupling of the two coordinates. The K_i and the F_{ij} coefficients are the second derivatives of the energy,

$$K_i = F_{ii} = \partial^2 E/\partial S_i^2 \quad F_{ij} = \partial^2 E/\partial S_i \partial S_j \tag{2.6}$$

The terms of higher order in the ΔS_i are similarly made up of coefficients proportional to third derivatives of the energy and third powers of deformations, fourth derivatives and fourth powers, and so on. For small enough deformations ΔS_i, it is a reasonable approximation to truncate the series expansion after the second-order terms. This is the *harmonic approximation*, thus named because it would be exact if the forces along every coordinate behaved like the forces in ideal springs or harmonic oscillators. The higher-order terms introduce *anharmonicity*, whose effects can be observed and evaluated in experiments. Generally these effects are small, but if molecules become highly excited and the deformations ΔS_i are large enough, the anharmonic contributions may be non-negligible.

From a practical point of view, what must be done to make use of the energy expression in the form given here is to choose a coordinate set for the S_i, and then determine values of the coefficients K_i and F_{ij}. We would then have a description of the energy and the intramolecular forces for a small neighborhood of space surrounding the minimum-energy conformation. As we will see in the next section, it has become customary to go quite a bit farther: by choosing our S_i in a chemically intuitive way, we try to use the energy expression over much larger regions of space, including alternative local minima and the transition paths between local minima. It is a good idea to remember, as one goes further into applications, that approximations and assumptions have been made, and that one aspect of evaluating results obtained from energy-function methods should always be to examine the correctness or appropriateness of these approximations.

At this point it should be noted that the energy expression here is quite a lot more general than "balls and springs." If the S_i referred only to the chemical bonds, then the harmonic truncation would represent point-masses connected by ideal Hooke's-law springs. Including other chemically reasonable terms, such as valence angles, torsion angles, and nonbonded interactions, makes the force field much more general and realistic.

2.2   Factors Differentiating Various Formulations of Force Fields

In this section we show how to classify and compare different empirical energy expressions and their formulations. The attributes involved, each of which are subject to choices or individual interpretation, are as follows:

- *Coordinates:* how are the S_i chosen?
- *Degree of expansion:* where is the formal Taylor series expression for the energy truncated?
- *Functional forms:* what are the detailed functional forms used to describe the forces for each type of coordinate?
- *Atom types:* how are variations of chemical valence differentiated and accounted for?
- *Data for parameterization:* what is the set of data used to calibrate the energy expression?
- *Goals:* for which applications is a force field designed?

While choices of these factors do not modify the basic concepts of empirical force fields set forth above, they can make significant differences in the results and operations of a force field. They also represent factors of which the practitioner must be aware if he is to understand fully what is being modeled. These factors also provide a basis for a taxonomy of force fields, permitting objective comparisons of their suitability for various problems [29].

2.2.1 Coordinates

Strictly speaking, the most appropriate choice of coordinates would be the set of $3N - 6$ *normal coordinates* derived from vibrational analysis of the molecule; they are complete in the sense that they are exactly the right number to define the internal geometry of the molecule, and they are not redundant. Spectroscopic force fields are usually expressed this way.

For convenience and intuitive appeal, however, most people find it desirable to think in terms of *internal coordinates*, namely, the bond lengths, bond angles (or valence angles), torsional angles, and nonbonded degrees of freedom familiar to chemists. This set of coordinates has significant redundance, especially in the way most present-day force fields are implemented; instead of $3N - 6$ coordinates (recall that N is the number of atoms in the molecule), there are typically about $5N$ or more terms representing the covalent structure and almost $N^2/2$ nonbonded terms. This redundancy causes difficulties in obtaining an unambiguous set of parameters that can be transferred among molecules with varying chemical compositions [39].

While there are other possible choices of coordinate system, we will adopt the internal coordinate system since it essentially dominates present-day approaches to molecular modeling of polymers and other systems. One important category of force fields involves only torsional and nonbonded coordinates; bonds are assumed to have a rigid, fixed length, and bond angles are also fixed at standardized values. In many situations this is a reasonable approximation, since the relatively stiffer bonds and angles are not as easily distorted from their normal values as the torsion angles are; but in other cases, even a few degrees of change in a set of bond angles can have a major effect on the overall conformation. Fixed bond lengths and bond angles introduce some technical difficulties into the procedures of energy minimization and molecular dynamics, as they represent constraints that the system must satisfy.

If we consider one of the S_i to represent a chemical bond, then the diagonal term for that coordinate, $K_i(\Delta S_i)^2$, can be written in a more familiar form by realizing that $\Delta S_i = R - R_0$; then the term becomes

$$E_{\text{bond}} = K_b(R - R_0)^2 \tag{2.7}$$

where R_0 is some reference length or zero-strain value for the bond in question. This is just the potential discussed above for the prototypical diatomic molecule. We use the symbol K_b to make it clear that this coefficient is for the stretch or compression of a bondlength. The slope of this potential function is $2K_b(R - R_0)$, as is clear from differentiating with respect to R; the slope is zero at the minimum point, $R = R_0$. The curvature at $R = R_0$ is $2K_b$, as is seen by differentiating again with respect to R. Similarly, a bond angle contribution can be written as

$$E_{\text{angle}} = K_\theta(\theta - \theta_0)^2 \tag{2.8}$$

where again θ_0 is the reference value for the angle. These terms are harmonic or second order just as in the formal expression. A system with bonding potentials only would correspond to the "balls-and-springs" model mentioned at the end of Section 2.1.

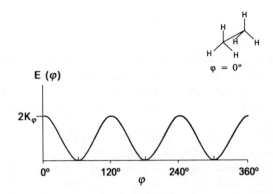

E (φ)

Figure 2.4. The three-fold ethane-type torsional energy is well represented by the trigonometric function $E(\varphi) = K_\varphi [1 + \cos(n\varphi - \delta)$ **with** $n = 3$ **and** $\delta = 0$.

We could write an analogous term for torsion angles, but here chemical experience enters to modify this choice. It is known that rotation about single bonds can involve quite small barriers in some cases, and we have the idea that the torsional potential should be some sort of periodic function similar to the three-fold form familiar from ethane (Fig. 2.4). It has become customary therefore to introduce a trigonometric expression for torsional degrees of freedom; the simplest case of this is an expression such as

$$E_{\text{torsion}} = K_\varphi[1 + \cos(n\varphi - \delta)] \tag{2.9}$$

Here the barrier height varies from 0 to $2K_\varphi$ as the cosine term varies from -1 to 1. The parameter n controls the periodicity of the function (e.g., $n = 3$ produces the three-fold function of Fig. 2.4), and the "phase shift" δ can be seen as a simple mathematical device to make the minima fall where we want them. More complicated expressions use a sum of terms with different values of K_φ, n, and δ to obtain potentials that are not simple sinusoidal curves; for example

$$E_{\text{torsion}} = \sum_n [(-1)^n V_n \cos(n\varphi)] \quad \text{for} \quad n = 0, 1, 2, 3, \ldots \tag{2.10}$$

The nonbonded interactions are functions of the distances between pairs of atoms that are not bonded to each other. It is customary in most approaches to exclude also interactions between atoms that are bonded to a common atom, thus excluding the outer atoms of a bond angle (Fig. 2.5). Thus the so-called 1-3 interactions are not considered in the list of nonbonded interactions.

Some formulations also exclude 1-4 interactions, that is, those which are at the extremities of a torsion angle (Fig. 2.6). It is difficult to show whether this is correct (because the 1-4 interactions are already taken care of by the torsional term) or not (because the torsional term is something "intrinsic" to the central bond). Much work has been done to study quantum-mechanical molecular energies and decompose them into constituents that can serve as analogs for empirical energy terms, but the

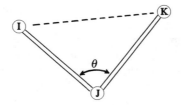

Figure 2.5. 1,3-interactions (e.g., $I - K$) are excluded from the list of nonbonded interactions.

situation is inconclusive. As we shall see, once one has chosen a convention as to where to start counting nonbonded interactions, the important job is to fit the energy expression to experimental data so as to have a consistent and accurate model.

The nonbonded interactions are usually taken to consist of a steric and an electrostatic component. The steric component, or van der Waals interaction, for one pair of atoms i and j can be represented by a Lennard-Jones n–m potential,

$$E_{ij}(\text{van der Waals}) = A_{ij}/R_{ij}^n - B_{ij}/R_{ij}^m \tag{2.11}$$

where n and m are integers, R_{ij} is the separation between the two nuclei, and the parameters A_{ij} and B_{ij} are specific to the pair of atoms i and j. The most commonly seen form is the 12-6 potential where n is 12 and m is 6.

The electrostatic component is written in terms of the partial atomic charges q_i and q_j on the two atoms,

$$E_{ij}(\text{electrostatic}) = Cq_iq_j/\varepsilon R_{ij} \tag{2.12}$$

Here C is a conversion factor which puts the result in the correct units, and ε is a dielectric constant or shielding factor. Strictly speaking, there is no well-formulated concept of a dielectric constant at a microscopic level as we are considering here, but the factor is included as a means of reducing the charged interactions at larger distances. One common approximation is to consider ε to be a function of the interatomic distance and to set $\varepsilon(R) = K \cdot R_{ij}$ where K is a constant. Then the denominator of the electrostatic expression contains an even power of R_{ij}, which allows convenience in programming the expression [40].

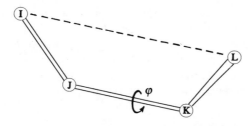

Figure 2.6. 1,4-interactions (e.g., $I - L$) are included as nonbonded interactions in some force fields, but not in others.

As the number of atoms in the system under consideration grows, the nonbonded terms begin to be the most numerous, and their evaluation requires the greatest expenditure of computer time. The number of each type of internal coordinate grows approximately linearly with system size, while the nonbonded contributions number a little less than $N \cdot (N - 1)/2$, i.e., they increase as the square of the number of atoms. In early calculations it was necessary, due to computer limitations, to impose an arbitrary cut-off distance. Interactions with R_{ij} greater than this distance, typically 8 Å, were simply ignored. For van der Waals forces, that is not a very serious error; for electrostatic interactions the $1/R_{ij}$ dependence means that the interaction energy falls slowly with increasing distance, and the cut-off approximation is more severe. Any cut-off implies a discontinuity, which can have serious consequences in simulations. This has occasioned a variety of approaches, including smoothing functions to remove discontinuities, and keeping larger numbers of nonbonded interactions.

To summarize, once the decision has been made to express the empirical energy in terms of internal coordinates, it has become customary to define a set which is formally redundant but looks chemically complete. This chemically intuitive set of coordinates includes every bond, bond angle, and torsional angle, as well as a set of nonbonded interactions that excludes only certain nearby atoms whose interactions are assumed to be accounted for by the other terms. As already pointed out, this model is considerably more than "balls and springs." The variety of additional restraining potentials which correspond to the chemically intuitive degrees of freedom makes a much more realistic molecular energy model.

2.2.2   Degree of Expansion

As indicated above, the energy expression is developed from a formal series expansion about a minimum energy point. We have described the harmonic approximation, which includes terms up to the second power in the deformations ΔS_i. Examples of such terms are the simple harmonic expressions for bond stretching and bond angle bending,

$$E_{\text{bond}} = K_b(R - R_0)^2 \qquad E_{\text{angle}} = K_\theta(\theta - \theta_0)^2 \qquad (2.13)$$

Strictly following this format would require the torsions to have a similar form such as $E_{\text{torsion}} = K_\varphi(\varphi - \varphi_0)^2$. It is clear that the use of a trigonometric form as introduced above goes beyond the harmonic approximation and introduces a certain amount of anharmonicity in the energy function. The same is true of the nonbonded functional forms. The fact is that while the series expansion form is valid for a small region about a local minimum, the choices for functional forms have been dominated by our ideas of what we plan to do with the energy expression later. To some extent, the justification of this departure is in the results obtained.

Higher-order terms can easily be written. In analogy to the harmonic terms for bonds and angles, we could use the cubic terms

$$E_{\text{bond}} = K_b(R - R_0)^3 \qquad E_{\text{angle}} = K_\theta(\theta - \theta_0)^3 \qquad (2.14)$$

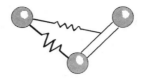

Figure 2.7. Pictorial representation of the coupling of a bond stretch and a valence angle bend.

Quartic terms follow the same pattern. Work has been done with such higher-order terms; the cubic terms are used especially often as the lowest-order terms that introduce anharmonicity directly into the bond and bond angle expressions.

2.2.3   Cross-Terms

So far in this discussion we have considered only those interactions that are of a given order in a single coordinate, such as the harmonic or cubic bond functions. The resulting force field can be termed *diagonal*, in the sense that only the diagonal coefficients (the K_i) of the general force constant matrix F_{ij} are present. We have omitted terms which reach the second or higher order by virtue of multiplying two or more first-order terms in different coordinates. These are the so-called *cross-terms*, since they mix or couple the effects of more than one coordinate. These terms are simply the last part of the second-order series expansion, Eq. (2.3) above, where they were written $F_{ij}(\Delta S_i)(\Delta S_j)$.

It is easy to suggest internal coordinate-based forms for these terms. An interaction of a bond with a valence angle, for instance, could be written

$$E_{\text{bond, angle}} = K_{R,\theta}(R - R_0)(\theta - \theta_0) \tag{2.15}$$

See Fig. 2.7 for an illustration of this interaction. Note that each coordinate enters only as the first power so that the term as a whole is of the second order. Similarly, an angle-torsion interaction, such as that pictured in Fig. 2.8, could be written

$$E_{\text{angle, torsion}} = K_{\theta,\varphi}(\theta - \theta_0)(\varphi - \varphi_0) \tag{2.16}$$

Alternatively one could use a trigonometric term for the torsional part of Eq. (2.16). There could also be cross terms between two different bonds, as shown in Fig. 2.9; the corresponding expression would be

$$E_{\text{bond, bond}} = K_{R,S}(R - R_0)(S - S_0) \tag{2.17}$$

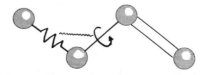

Figure 2.8. Pictorial representation of the coupling of a bond angle and a valence torsion.

Figure 2.9. Pictorial representation of the coupling between two adjacent bonds.

where R and S denote bondlengths of different bonds. Similarly, terms can be written for the interactions of one angle with another, one torsion with another, and bonds with torsions. Taken together, these different quadratic forms, some of second order in a single variable, others the product of two first-order terms, make up the full general quadratic expansion of the energy expression in terms of internal coordinates.

What do the cross-terms represent physically? Whereas the straightforward harmonic bond function signifies the similarity of the chemical bond to an ideal spring for small stretching or compression, the cross-terms account for the interactions of different internal coordinates as shown in Figs. 2.7 through 2.9. Chemical intuition supports the idea that changes in the bond angle I-J-K should affect the strengths of the I-J and J-K bonds, for example. The magnitudes and signs of the coefficients of these terms express how much coupling there is and whether it acts as a reinforcement or a reduction.

Are cross-terms necessary? This depends on the requirements placed on the force field. Logically, the addition of the cross-terms should lead to a more flexible force field better able to fit a wide variety of data, simply because more parameters and functional forms are present. In cases where a full second-order parameter set has been determined, the cross-terms are not zero, but neither are they very large, amounting to perhaps 10% of the diagonal terms in magnitude. On the other hand, the presence of these extra parameters increases the size of the parameter-determination job, and slightly increases the execution time of programs. There is no unequivocal answer, and cross-terms have been a matter of some controversy between proponents of different force fields [29].

2.2.4   Functional Forms

The simple functional forms set forth here are certainly not the only ones that could be used, and indeed many others have been introduced in various formulations. Some of the more common ones have been collected in Table 2.1.

2.2.5   Atom Types

Each of the energy terms enumerated above refers to the deformation of some internal coordinate, which is defined by its constituent atoms. Each term contains empirical

Table 2.1 Functional Forms Commonly Used in Empirical Force Fields

Bond stretching/compression

(1) $K_b(r - r_0)^2$ hormonic

(2) $K_b(r - r_0)^2[1 + k_1(r - r_0)]$ cubic anharmonic term

(3) $K_b(r - r_0)^2 [1 + k_1(r - r_0) + k_2(r - r_0)^2]$ quartic term

(4) $D[1 - \exp(-A(r - r_0))]^2$ Morse function

Bond angle bending

(1) $K_\theta(\theta - \theta_0)^2$ harmonic in θ

(2) $K_\theta(\cos\theta - \cos\theta_0)^2$ harmonic in $\cos\theta$

(3) $K_\theta(\theta - \theta_0)^2 + F(q - q_0)^2 + F'(q - q_0)$ Urey-Bradley form, where q is the 1–3 distance (i.e., the distance I-K in the angle I-J-K)

(4) $K_\theta(\theta - \theta_0)^2[1 + \sum\limits_{n=1}^{4} k_n(\theta - \theta_0)^n]$ anharmonicity as powers of $\Delta\theta$

Torsions

(1) $K_\varphi[1 + \cos(n\varphi - \delta)]$ One-term trigonometric form

(2) $\sum V_n \cos(n\varphi)$ Trigonometric series

(3) $\sum V_n \cos^n \varphi$ Trigonometric power series

(4) $K_\tau(\tau - \tau_0)^2$ Simple harmonic form sometimes used for improper torsions

Nonbonded interactions

(1) $q_i q_j / \varepsilon r_{ij}$ Coulombic interaction with dielectric constant ε

(2) $A/r^{12} - B/r^6$ Lennard-Jones 12–6 potential

(3) $A/r^9 - B/r^6$ Lennard-Jones 9–6 potential

(4) $A/r^{12} - B/r^{10}$ Sometimes used for distance-dependence of hydrogen bond

(5) $A/r^n - B/r^m$ General form of Lennard-Jones n–m potential

(6) $A \exp(-Br/r_0) - C/r^6$ Exponential-6 potential

(7) $D[\exp(-2A(r - r_0)) - 2 \exp(-A(r - r_0))]$ Morse form

Cross-terms can be formed by multiplying terms in any combination of powers. The simplest involve only a single term for each coordinate, e.g., one bond function multiplied by one angular function. The Urey-Bradley form, bond angle function (3), couples both bonds with the angle they form by virtue of its dependence on the 1-3 distance which depends on both the angle and the bondlengths.

energy parameters: the various coefficients K_b, K_θ, K_φ (and if present the cross-term coefficients such as $K_{R\theta}$); the zero-strain values R_0 and θ_0; the A_{ij} and B_{ij} coefficients of the Lennard-Jones part of the nonbonded potential; and the partial charges q_i. We have the choice of simply assigning unique parameters to each term, or of trying to group terms in a chemically consistent fashion. Grouping the terms involves the process of assigning atom types to each atom in the system.

The choice of atom types determines the sensitivity of the force field to distinctions among chemical environments. A minimal set of carbon atom types would include just sp^3, sp^2, sp, and aromatic carbons. More detailed force fields distinguish as many as 20 or more carbon types, representing different ring sizes, resonance possibilities, and substituents. For large molecules, extended or united atoms are sometimes used; these are artificial constructs that represent a non-hydrogen atom plus all the hydrogens attached to it. The masses of united atoms include the hydrogen masses, and the parameters involving them are adjusted to model the real system as well as possible.

A large atom type set, while providing detailed recognition of subtly different chemical environments, complicates the job of developing a parameter set. If there are, say, 100 different atom types, then it is possible to form 100×100 bond types and $100 \times 100 \times 100$ bond angle types. Not all of these actually exist or are needed for any calculation, but there will still be many bond types and very many angle types, and each of these requires corresponding energy parameters.

2.2.6   Data Used for Fitting

The meaning of *empirical* when applied to force fields is that they are derived by adjusting the parameters in the energy function so that calculated quantities agree with experimental data. The data can be geometric measurements, vibrational frequencies, rotation barriers, heats of formation and other thermodynamic quantities, crystal packing geometries, and other observables. In recent years, results calculated from *ab initio* quantum mechanics have also been used as a means of deriving parameters. The choice of data used influences the characteristics of the force field and its suitability for various applications.

The general approach to parameter development is depicted schematically in Fig. 2.10. Starting values for unknown parameters can often be guessed on the basis of similarity to other known parameters or estimated by chemical reasoning about the restoring forces involved. Calculations are made to compute the desired quantities for a group of molecules for which experimental or *ab initio* computed data are readily available. The discrepancies are noted and the parameters adjusted so as to reduce them. To some extent this process can be automated, but in many cases manual intervention is required, if only to inform the fitting process which calculated datum

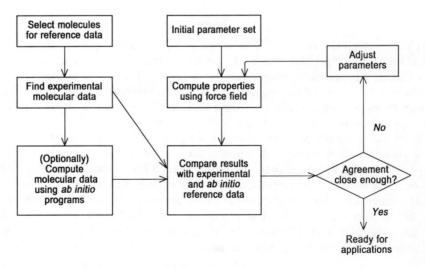

Figure 2.10. Schematic of the parameter development process.

corresponds to which experimental one. The process is continued until a satisfactory total mean squared residual (or maximum individual residual) is obtained.

One major origin of force fields was the desire of physical organic chemists to compute thermodynamic properties and to quantitate the notion of strain energy as a factor in reactivity. Related topics such as rotational isomers, energy barriers and surfaces, and transition states are consistent with this approach. The alternative development of empirical force fields as a means of fitting vibrational spectra placed more emphasis on the force constants. If the atoms are considered as classical point masses moving under the influence of a force field, then classical mechanics prescribes how to determine the vibrational modes and frequencies of the system.

It stands to reason that if a force field is to be used primarily to generate minimum-energy conformations, there is no need to parameterize it to reproduce vibrational data (which are related to the curvatures of the energy surface near the local minimum). If one is interested in barrier heights and energy surfaces, the detailed shape of the potential near the minima is not as important as the ability to model the interactions that produce the main features of the surfaces. But if one wants to consider the dynamical processes whereby the system crosses the energy barriers or moves about on the energy surfaces, then the detailed shape of the barrier is important, while details of the geometry at the two local minima on either side of the barrier may not be so critical.

A key assumption is that once a force field has been parameterized with respect to a certain set of data, it is applicable to other molecules not in the fitting set. This attribute, called transferability, is not automatically assured by a skillful fitting job alone. A force field developed with reference to hydrocarbons embodies no information about functional groups that would be encountered in ketones, aldehydes, peptides, etc. The new parameters required would have to be determined by a new fitting process or defaulted to some reasonable estimates.

Ab initio programs offer the possibility of obtaining large bodies of uniformly accurate data, including hard-to-observe data:

- calculations at different conformers can show the variation of geometric entities such as bond lengths and bond angles, as well as vibrational shifts as a function of conformation [41];
- calculations using slightly distorted (non-equilibrium) geometries can give information about forces and anharmonicity of the energy surface [42].

Most calculations done in the parameter development process consider isolated molecules in vacuum, and little is learned about intermolecular forces. Accordingly, it is useful to consider some form of data, such as crystal packing or liquid-state data, that involve significant intermolecular nonbonded interactions. A two-stage parameter determination process is sometimes used: first a set of nonbonded interactions are determined by calculating crystal structures, using rigid model geometries of the monomers. Then with the nonbonded parameters fixed, efforts are concentrated on fitting the covalent skeletal degrees of freedom. The process can be iterated to self-consistency.

Increasingly, the trend in modern force field developments is to include more and more consistency, that is, to develop the force field so that it fits more different types

Table 2.2 Characteristics of Some Empirical Force Fields
The information in this table is highly summarized. Refer to the text and the reference for details.

Force field	Ref.	Coordi-nates	Degree of expansion	Functional forms	Atom types	Data used for fitting	Design goals
AMBER	(a)	Cartesian	Quadratic	Diagonal plus torsions, nonbonded	Many, varied	Geometry, vibrations	Proteins and nucleic acids; derived from CFF[b]
CHARMM	(c)	Cartesian	Quadratic	Same as above	Many, varied	Geometry, vibrations, alternate minima	Same as above
DISCOVER	(d)	Cartesian	Quadratic plus some higher terms	As above, plus optional cross-terms	Many, varied	Geometry, vibrations, *ab initio*, crystal packing	Same as above
DREIDING	(e)	Cartesian	Quadratic	Diagonal plus torsions, nonbonded	Minimal	Geometry, torsion barriers	Generality, with prescription for new parameters
ECEPP	(f)	Torsions	Trigono-metric	Torsions, nonbonded	Moderate	Torsion barriers, nonbonded interactions	Simple energy form for calculations in torsion space, rigid geometry
JUMNA	(g)	Helical coords	Trigono-metric	Simple forms based on helical coords	Limited	Geometry, torsion barriers	Base sequence-dependent effects in nucleic acids
MM2/MM3	(h)	Cartesian	Quadratic plus higher	Explicit cross-terms	Many, varied	Geometry, vibrations, heats of formation	Accurate small-molecule force field
TRIPOS	(i)	Cartesian	Quadratic	Diagonal plus torsions, nonbonded	Minimal	Geometry, rotamer energies	Simple, fairly general field for small organics and proteins
UFF	(j)	Cartesian	Quadratic	Diagonal plus torsions, nonbonded	Minimal	Geometry, torsion barriers	Rules to set parameters simply for entire periodic table

References:
(a) AMBER: P. K. Weiner and P. A. Kollman, *J. Comp. Chem.* **2**, 287–303 (1981), AMBER: Assisted model building with energy refinement. A general program for modeling molecules and their interactions; S. J. Weiner, P. A. Kollman, D. A. Case, U. C. Singh, C. Ghio, G. Alagona, S. Profeta, and P. Weiner, *J. Am. Chem. Soc.* **106**, 765–784 (1984), A new force field for molecular mechanical simulation of nucleic acids and proteins; S. J. Weiner, P. A. Kollman, D. T. Nguyen, and D. A. Case, *J. Comp. Chem.* **7**, 230–252 (1986), An all atom force field for simulations of proteins and nucleic acids.

(b) Ref. 38.

(c) CHARMM: B. R. Brooks. R. E. Bruccoleri. B. D. Olafson, D. J. States, S. Swaminathan, and M. Karplus, *J. Comp. Chem.* **4**, 187–217 (1983), CHARMM: A program for macromolecular energy, minimization, and dynamics calculations; L. Nilsson and M. Karplus, *J. Comp. Chem.* **7**, 591–616 (1986), Empirical energy functions for energy minimization and dynamics of nucleic acids; see also Ref. 41.

(d) DISCOVER is a trademark of Biosym Technologies, Inc. (San Diego, CA). See Ref. 42.

(e) Ref. 43.

(f) ECEPP: F. A. Momany, R. F. McGuire, A. W. Burgess, and H. A. Scheraga, *J. Phys. Chem.* **79**, 2361–2381 (1975), Energy parameters in polypeptides. VII. geometric parameters, partial atomic charges, nonbonded interactions, hydrogen bond interactions, and intrinsic torsional potentials for the naturally occurring amino acids.

(g) JUMNA: R. Lavery in Structure & Expression, Vol. 3: DNA Bending and Curvature (W. K. Olson, M. H. Sarma. R. H. Sarma, and M. Sundaralingam, Eds.), Adenine Press (1988), 191–211, Junctions and bends in nucleic acids: A new theoretical modeling approach.

(h) MM2: N. L. Allinger, *J. Am. Chem. Soc.* **99**, 8127–8132 (1977), Conformational analysis. 130. MM2. A hydrocarbon force field utilizing V_1 and V_2 torsional terms. MM3: N. L. Allinger, Y. H. Yuh, and J-H. Lii, *J. Am. Chem. Soc.* **111**, 8551–8566 (1989), Molecular mechanics. The MM3 force field for hydrocarbons. 1.

(i) TRIPOS: M. Clark, R. D. Cramer III, and N. Van Opdenbosch, *J. Comp. Chem.* **10**, 982–1012 (1989), Validation of the general purpose Tripos 5.2 force field.

(j) UFF: A. K. Rappé, C. J. Casewit, K. S. Colwell, W. A. Goddard III, and W. M. Skiff, *J. Am. Chem. Soc.* **114**, 10024–10035 (1992), UFF, a full periodic table force field for molecular mechanics and molecular dynamics simulations.

of data: gas and condensed phase; thermodynamic, geometric, and spectral data; and experimental and calculated information.

2.2.7   Goals of a Force Field

Ideally, one would like a force field to be as simple, accurate, and general as possible, as well as easy (from the point of view of software and programming) to implement, maintain, and expand. Because these desirable characteristics are generally in conflict with each other, there have evolved a number of different approaches representing different types of compromises.

Simplicity refers to the form and degree of expansion of the energy expression, as well as to the multiplicity of atom types defined. The DREIDING force field [43] places a high premium on simplicity by choosing a minimal atom type set, using simple harmonic terms, and standardizing most parameters. For example, the stretching force constant for all single bonds is 700 kcal/mol-$Å^2$, regardless of the chemical details of the bond (double and triple bonds have double or triple this force constant), and all bond angles have a bending force constant of 100 kcal/mol-rad^2. The rationale for this approach is two-fold: first, it makes it straightforward to develop parameters for every element in the periodic table; and second, most conformational flexibility is expressed in the softer torsional and nonbonded modes, and more effort is put into accurate estimates of those parameters. This force field is reasonably reliable at computing equilibrium geometries, but little confidence can be put in vibrational or dynamic data derived from it.

Naturally, increasing the accuracy and generality would require more detailed functional forms, higher degrees of expansion, and cross-terms. A more detailed atom type set would also be needed to distinguish more finely among different chemical situations. The result would be a large set of parameters and a more difficult implementation job. Documenting a more complete force field, and explaining to the user how to modify and update it, would be correspondingly more exacting tasks. Among commercial software vendors there has been continual competition and maneuvering over the factors of simplicity, accuracy, and generality. There is a dearth of refereed, published work which correctly compares the up-to-date force field formulations of vendors in a consistent manner [29].

2.2.8   Characteristics of Some Published Force Fields

Having outlined the choices available to the designer of a force field, we are now in a position to classify some of the more well-known force fields according to this taxonomy. This is done in Table 2.2. Obviously this is only a cursory classification; to understand a force field, one must study it in much more detail, and the comparison of two force fields is a task that should be undertaken with completeness and caution. Subject to this warning, Table 2.2 simply attempts to clarify some of the basic design aspects of commonly used (and in some cases commercially available) force fields. When examining a new force field, the student or prospective user will be aided by first undertaking such a clarification and by examining the other force field attributes set forth in this chapter.

2.3   Summary

The empirical force field model describes the motions of the nuclei (or the atoms, considered as point masses and ignoring the electrons) with simple functional forms corresponding to commonly recognized chemical entities such as bonds, valence angles, torsion angles, and nonbonded interactions. The numbers and types of such functional forms depends on the implementation and the purposes envisioned by the force field designer. At his disposal are the choices of coordinate system used to describe molecules, the degree of expansion of functional forms, the use or omission of cross-terms, the atom types differentiated, and the data used to determine the parameters. There exist today a considerable variety of force fields, and the factors listed can be used to make cursory comparisons among them. However, force fields are not simple, and there are few examples of careful comparisons over a wide range of molecules and applications.

3

Calculations with Force Fields

The purpose of this chapter is to acquaint the reader with the common operations performed with force fields, and with the calculation processes, in sufficient detail to provide an understanding of factors that affect the outcome. In this approach we will describe the input requirements that must be met in order to start a calculation and give an idea of the magnitudes of different calculations. This introduction describes the techniques which are taken for granted throughout the rest of the book, and it is essential to an understanding of how applications are approached.

To enumerate the details fairly completely, we have chosen a small organic molecule with several different types of atoms, and have mimicked the processes which once were done manually, but now are done automatically with computer software. It is a great convenience that computers can now do these tedious bookkeeping tasks, but it useful to go through one example and understand the meticulous preparation required to carry out force field calculations. It also helps illustrate assumptions and conventions that can have an effect on the results.

Generalization from small-molecule to macromolecule calculations is straightforward as soon as one introduces the concept of molecular fragments that are easily defined (because they are small), then are automatically linked together to supply the complete definition of the macromolecule. In this approach, frequently used fragments, such as a library of monomers, can be defined once for all future uses.

We will begin by showing the molecule in various shorthand notations and indicating how the input for calculations is prepared. We will then discuss or describe the evaluation of the energy function and its derivatives, energy minimization, the mapping of torsional barriers and surfaces, conformational search, vibrational analysis, and molecular dynamics. A familiarity and fluency with these operations is required for the rest of the book.

3.1 Setting Up the Calculation

Our molecule for these examples will be methyl acetate (Fig. 3.1). This molecule has only three chemical elements, carbon, hydrogen, and oxygen, but it necessitates the differentiation of five atom types because there are two chemically distinct carbons atoms (in the methyl and carbonyl groups) and two distinct oxygens (carbonyl and ether).

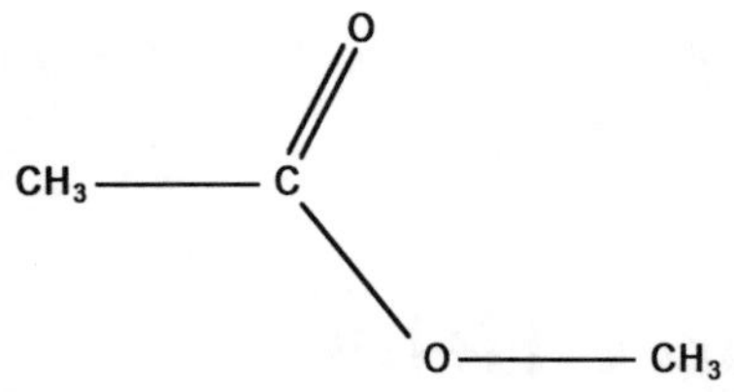

Figure 3.1. Methyl acetate.

To get started, we need three sets of data:

- a starting geometry, that is, a list of the Cartesian coordinates for each atom
- an enumeration of every term in the energy function, that is, a list of all internal coordinates and interactions that will contribute to the conformational energy
- a set of energy parameters for these interactions.

3.1.1   Starting Geometry

For a small molecule such as our example, it is not hard to make up approximate Cartesian coordinates for a simple planar conformation. The molecule can simply be sketched on graph paper, using reasonably accurate bond lengths and angles, and the in-plane coordinates can be measured. Simple trigonometry will give approximate coordinates for the out-of-plane atoms. In general, this tedious task has been completely automated by computer programs. Some programs operate graphically and tidy up approximate sketches (i.e., they make all lines straight, they force bonds and angles to reasonable values, and they observe some simple valence rules); others work from a structural description of the molecule and generate a conformation using chemical and geometrical rules. Sophisticated rule-based programs have been developed that are capable of generating reasonable geometries for quite complex or highly constrained molecules [44, 45].

Suffice it to say here that one must have a completely enumerated starting geometry; every atom must be assigned starting coordinates. In the case of polymeric systems, this can be a formidable task. Poor choices of monomer geometries or overly simple replication of units can impose some undesirable geometric regularities or periodicities which must be modified.

3.1.2   Enumeration of the Energy Terms

Working here with internal coordinates, we can enumerate lists of energy terms by simple visual inspection. In Fig. 3.2 the sample molecule is redrawn to show a sequencing system for the atoms. It makes no difference in what sequence the atoms are numbered, as long as we are consistent throughout the calculation. It may be of value, when working with a series of molecules, to observe a consistent scheme (e.g.,

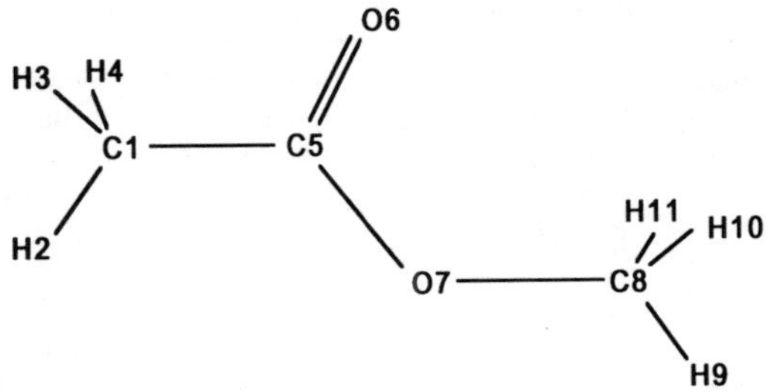

Figure 3.2. Methyl acetate with sequence numbers assigned arbitrarily to the atoms.

numbering skeletal or non-hydrogen atoms similarly in all the structures), but it is not a necessity.

In Table 3.1 we have listed all the different types of atoms we shall recognize in this calculation. There are five atom types: one type of hydrogen, two kinds of carbons, and two kinds of oxygens. This is not the only choice possible; some programs may differentiate between the two methyl carbons because of the different species to which they are attached. Thus the atom typing has already introduced certain choices into the calculation at this early stage.

Table 3.2 lists the 11 atoms in the molecule, assigns the atom type index number (from Table 3.1) to each one, and gives a partial atomic charge to be used in electrostatic calculations. Several "numbers" must be kept track of: the left column of Table 3.2 is the sequence number of the atom within the molecule, an arbitrary sequencing choice. The third column is the chemical type index from Table 3.1, which is a convention that must be followed in calculations on other molecules.

The partial atomic charges can be derived in a variety of ways. Some algorithms are based on the chemical situation and bonding partners around each atom. Another method is to perform a simple semiempirical quantum mechanical calculation (such as CNDO/INDO, which would take only a few seconds for this molecule), which includes a population analysis and directly lists the excess or deficit electron population for each atom. More sophisticated methods work from the quantum-mechanically calculated molecular electrostatic potential, fitting a set of point atomic charges that best reproduce this spatial density [46]. It should be noted that the placement of point charges on atoms is an approximation in itself (in fact, it is the

Table 3.1 Atom Types in Methyl Acetate

Chemical situation	Index number
H	1
Methyl carbon	2
Carbonyl carbon	3
Ester oxygen	4
Carbonyl oxygen	5

Table 3.2 Designation of Atoms in Methyl Acetate

Sequence number	Chemical element	Atom type index	Partial charge
1	C	2	−0.06
2	H	1	0.02
3	H	1	0.02
4	H	1	0.02
5	C	3	0.50
6	O	5	−0.40
7	O	4	−0.30
8	C	2	0.29
9	H	1	−0.03
10	H	1	−0.03
11	H	1	−0.03

monopole approximation to a mathematically exact multipole expansion), and further that maintaining a fixed set of atomic charges as the molecule deforms and vibrates is also a simplification. There has been some recent work in which charges are allowed to change as a molecule undergoes molecular dynamics [47, 48].

In Table 3.3 we have listed all the bonds in the molecule, indicating the atoms involved and repeating their atom type indices. We see that the ten bonds occur with five distinct combinations of atom types, to which we have assigned bond type numbers in order of occurrence. Enumerating the bonds is fairly simple for any structure that can be written down on paper, because each bond is separately drawn. Obviously it would be impractical to do this manually for large structures.

Angles and torsional terms are not as simple to do visually, but it is a straightforward and systematic process to enumerate them. Bond angles are enumerated in Table 3.4, much the way the bonds were. The result is a total of 16 bond angles defined for our molecule, representing 7 different types. Note that the convention

Table 3.3 Bond List for Methyl Acetate

Bond number	Atoms involved	Atom type indices	Bond type
1	C1–C5	2–3	1
2	C1–H2	2–1	2
3	C1–H3	2–1	2
4	C1–H4	2–1	2
5	C5–O6	3–5	3
6	C5–O7	3–4	4
7	O7–C8	4–2	5
8	C8–H9	2–1	2
9	C8–H10	2–1	2
10	C8–H11	2–1	2

Table 3.4 Bond Angle List for Methyl Acetate

Sequence number	Atom involved	Atom type indices	Angle type
1	H2–C1–C5	1–2–3	1
2	H3–C1–C5	1–2–3	1
3	H4–C1–C5	1–2–3	1
4	H2–C1–H3	1–2–1	2
5	H2–C1–H4	1–2–1	2
6	H3–C1–H4	1–2–1	2
7	C1–C5–O6	2–3–5	3
8	C1–C5–O7	2–3–4	4
9	O6–C5–O7	5–3–4	5
10	C5–O7–C8	3–4–2	6
11	O7–C8–H9	4–2–1	7
12	O7–C8–H10	4–2–1	7
13	O7–C8–H11	4–2–1	7
14	H9–C8–H10	1–2–1	1
15	H9–C8–H11	1–2–1	1
16	H10–C8–H11	1–2–1	1

followed is to include every angle about each center; thus carbon atom C1 is centered within six angles, three each of type H—C—C and H—C—H.

Torsion angles are listed in Table 3.5. Note here that the convention is again to include all possible torsions about a given bond. Thus for an ethane-type interaction there would be nine torsions involving the central bond. Here, where there is an sp^3—sp^2 bonding situation about the C1—C5 bond, there are six torsions. Clearly the torsional energy parameters must correctly take into account this multiplicity, and maintain similar conventions from molecule to molecule, or the torsional forces will be incorrectly estimated. Additionally, we have defined one "improper" torsion

Table 3.5 Torsional Angle List for Methyl Acetate

Sequence number	Atoms involved	Type indices of central atoms	Torsion type
1	H2–C1–C5–O6	2–3	1
2	H2–C1–C5–O7	2–3	1
3	H3–C1–C5–O6	2–3	1
4	H3–C1–C5–O7	2–3	1
5	H4–C1–C5–O6	2–3	1
6	H4–C1–C5–O7	2–3	1
7	C1–C5–O7–C8	3–4	2
8	O6–C5–O7–C8	3–4	2
9	C5–O7–C8–H9	4–2	3
10	C5–O7–C8–H10	4–2	3
11	C5–O7–C8–H11	4–2	3
12	C1–O7–C5–O6	(improper torsion)	4

angle. This is a means of assigning an energy contribution to out-of-plane deformations about the central carbonyl carbon atom C5. There are several ways to measure such an interaction. As the improper torsion is defined here, it measures the angle between the plane defined by atoms C1, C5, and O7 and the plane defined by atoms O7, C5, and O6. Another metric would be the distance of atom C5 from the plane defined by atoms C1, O7, and O6. Fig. 3.3 pictures the measurements involved in torsional angles.

The final energetic interactions to be enumerated are the nonbonded terms (see Table 3.6). These are pairwise interactions between atoms that are not bonded to each other nor to a common atom. Thus carbon C1 is "excluded" from interacting with six nearby atoms. Its first interactions are of the so-called 1–4 type, because there are two intervening atoms (three bonds). Some calculations also exclude 1–4 interactions, reasoning that they are accounted for by the torsional potentials of the central bond. Arguments exist in favor of both conventions; see the discussion in Sec. 2.2.1.

Note in Table 3.6 that the atoms are listed in sequence order, and that in deciding whether interactions can occur, only higher-numbered atoms are considered. This prevents double-counting of interactions. In computer programming, this type of ordered sum is straightforward to program. Note also that for this small molecule, the number of *excluded* interactions is almost as large as the number of allowed ones. As the chemical system grows larger, this balance shifts drastically so that there are many more interactions than exclusions.

In larger molecules the number of nonbonded interaction terms approaches the theoretical limit of $N \cdot (N - 1)/2$. For a macromolecule with 1,000 atoms, there would

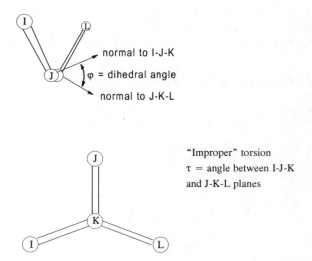

Figure 3.3. The dihedral angle is the angle between the two planes I-J-K and J-K-L (calculated as the angle between the two normals to these planes). The "improper" torsion expresses out-of-plane deformation.

Table 3.6 Nonbonded Interactions for Methyl Acetate

Atom number	Excluded from	Interacts with	Number of interactions
1	2, 3, 4, 5, 6, 7	8, 9, 10, 11	4
2	3, 4, 5	6, 7, 8, 9, 10, 11	6
3	4, 5	6, 7, 8, 9, 10, 11	6
4	5	6, 7, 8, 9, 10, 11	6
5	6, 7, 8	9, 10, 11	3
6	7	8, 9, 10, 11	4
7	8, 9, 10, 11	none	0
8	9, 10, 11	none	0
9	10, 11	none	0
10	11	none	0
	Total exclusions: 26	Total interactions:	29

be almost half a million nonbonded terms to evaluate. To reduce this number it has been customary to ignore any interactions longer than a certain cut-off distance, say 8 or 10 Å. The van der Waals interactions, falling off as r^{-6}, are very small beyond this distance, and for that part of the nonbonded interaction the cutoff is reasonable. But the electrostatic term decreases as r^{-1} and remains appreciable over a much longer range; it may not be a good approximation to ignore longer-range electrostatic effects.

Altogether there are 66 interactions that make up the conformational energy of this molecule. There are $N = 11$ atoms, so the minimum number of coordinates needed for a description of its internal coordinate space is $3 \times 11 - 6$ or 27; our interaction set is redundant by more than a factor of two.

3.1.3   Energy Parameters

We are now almost ready to begin calculations on our sample molecule. We assume that an initial geometry has been generated by one means or another, and we have enumerated all the terms in the energy function. The remaining ingredient is a set of energy parameters. As we have seen from Tables 3.3 through 3.6, there are 5 different types of bonds, 7 different types of angles, 4 types of torsions, and 7 types of nonbonded interaction. It is not necessary to prepare a complete table of parameters for every conceivable interaction type, but only for the ones actually present in this molecule; for example, only 5 bonds and 7 nonbonded interactions of the 15 possible combinations of five atom types actually occur. One of the functions of force-field computer programs is to enumerate such lists automatically and to notify the user if any necessary energy parameters are missing.

We will assume we are going to use the simple forms discussed in Chapter 2, with harmonic bond and angle terms, a one-term trigonometric torsion function, and both van der Waals and electrostatic terms for the nonbonded interactions. The energy function can be written as follows:

$$E = \sum K_b(R - R_0)^2 + \sum K_\theta(\theta - \theta_0)^2 + \sum K_\varphi[1 + \cos(n\varphi - \delta)]$$
$$+ \sum (A_{ij}/r_{ij}^{12} - B_{ij}/r_{ij}^6 + q_i q_j/\varepsilon r_{ij}) \tag{3.1}$$

For each type of bond we need values for K_b and R_0; for each angle, K_θ and θ_0; for each torsion we need K_φ, n, and δ; and we need the nonbonded parameters A_{ij} and B_{ij}, as well as the partial charges q_i and q_j. We will assume that a set of parameters appropriate for this molecule has been determined. As indicated in Chapter 2, there is some judgement required as to what is "appropriate." Parameter development needs to have been carried out using similar functional groups, homologous series, different levels of substitution, and uniformly good experimental data or *ab initio* calculations.

3.2   Applications of Empirical Energy Functions

Now we proceed with the basic operations of molecular mechanics and dynamics. The full detail of the internal coordinates of methyl acetate developed above will not be needed, but it will serve to make the concepts concrete. As we begin with evaluation of the energy, we will work in some detail; then as each step builds on the previous ones, we will be able to dispense with details and work at a more conceptual level.

3.2.1   Energy Calculation

The most fundamental operation with empirical force fields is to evaluate the energy at the current molecular geometry. This involves calculating the energy contribution from each term in the energy expression and accumulating the net result. As we go through the calculation schematically, we will see how the input data enumerated above comes into play.

To sum up the energy, we (or more accurately, the computer programs) begin with the bonded contribution. For our sample molecule, the sum contains ten terms, one for each bond listed in Table 3.3. For each bond in turn, the program determines the atoms i and j involved, obtains their current coordinates, and calculates the bond length using the Cartesian distance metric

$$R_{ij} = [(x_j - x_i)^2 + (y_j - y_i)^2 + (z_j - z_i)^2]^{1/2} \tag{3.2}$$

See Fig. 3.4. The program then obtains the atom indices and determines the bond type; it uses the type number to fetch the corresponding parameters from a list, and it calculates the energy contribution for the bond. The identical operations are repeated for each bond in the list.

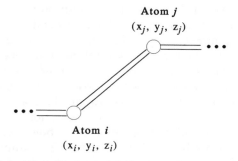

Figure 3.4. Evaluating the bond length between atoms i and j.

For the bond angles, the program needs to compute the value of the angle from the coordinates of the three constituent atoms; see Fig. 3.5. Denoting the atoms as i-j-k (where j is the central atom), the program computes the vectors $j \rightarrow i$ and $j \rightarrow k$ as direction numbers, then forms their dot product (or scalar product), which is equal to the magnitudes of the bondlengths times the cosine of the angle between them. That is, the components of the bond vectors are:

$$j \rightarrow i = [(x_i - x_j), (y_i - y_j), (z_i - z_j)] \tag{3.3a}$$

$$j \rightarrow k = [(x_k - x_j), (y_k - y_j), (z_k - z_j)] \tag{3.3b}$$

and the lengths of the bonds are:

$$R_{ji} = [(x_i - x_j)^2 + (y_i - y_j)^2 + (z_i - z_j)^2]^{1/2} \tag{3.4a}$$

$$R_{jk} = [(x_k - x_j)^2 + (y_k - y_j)^2 + (z_k - z_j)^2]^{1/2} \tag{3.4b}$$

Then the cosine of θ is obtained from the dot product of the bond vectors by the relation:

$$j \rightarrow i \cdot j \rightarrow k = R_{ji} R_{jk} \cos \theta \tag{3.5}$$

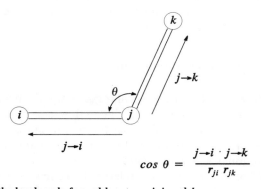

$$\cos \theta = \frac{j \rightarrow i \cdot j \rightarrow k}{r_{ji} \, r_{jk}}$$

Figure 3.5. Evaluating the bond angle formed by atoms i, j, and k.

Finally, the angle θ is extracted and the energy contribution $K_\theta(\theta - \theta_0)^2$ is calculated and added to the energy. This is repeated for each bond angle in the series.

Torsional angles require a series of similar, but still more tedious computations. In brief, if the torsion is denoted as *i-j-k-l*, the program first calculates the vector normal to the *i-j-k* plane and the vector normal to the *j-k-l* plane; the dot product of these normals equals the cosine of the torsion angle times the product of the magnitudes of the normal vectors, analogously to the dot product expression used for bond angles (see Eq. (3.5) and Fig. 3.3). Computation of the components of the vector normal to a plane involves obtaining the two bond vectors and forming their cross product (or vector product). The vector algebra is tedious but straightforward and, as usual, once the current value of the torsion angle is obtained, it is used to compute the energy contribution according to the formula chosen, in this case,

$$K_\varphi[1 + \cos(n\varphi - \delta)] \tag{3.6}$$

The nonbonded interactions depend only on the separation of the two atoms involved; calculating the separation is exactly the same as computing a bondlength with the Cartesian distance formula of Eq. (3.2). It is worth noting that with this formula we actually calculate r^2 first, not r; since the van der Waals expression contains only even powers of r, we can avoid taking square roots. But the Coulombic interaction, $q_i q_j / r$, has the first power of r in the denominator. This requires taking the square root of the calculated quantity r^2. In large molecules, where there are very many nonbonded interactions, these square roots add time to the calculation. One way to rationalize using r^2 in the denominator of the electrostatic expression is to consider a dielectric constant; the formula is then $q_i q_j / \varepsilon r$. There is no consistent definition of a microscopic dielectric constant, but one could consider that as r increases, there is more likely to be some dielectric effect from intervening atoms. The simplest model for this effect would be to consider $\varepsilon(r) = r$, i.e., a linear distance-dependent dielectric. This makes the electrostatic expression have the convenient form $q_i q_j / r^2$. Much work is done with this form of the dielectric constant, which was originally invented only to try to avoid taking the thousands of square roots that slowed down the calculations for large molecules [40].

We have now gone through every term contributing to the energy expression, and have accumulated the conformational or "strain" energy of the molecule for the current conformation and subject to the parameter set and structural elements used. We are now in a position to see what more can be done.

3.2.2   Derivatives and Energy Minimization

Having evaluated the energy for one molecular geometry, the next logical application of the empirical energy expression is to find a low-energy conformation of the molecule. This involves mathematical prescriptions for shifting the atoms in space so as to lower the energy and eventually bring the molecule to the local minimum nearest in conformational space to where it started. In the context of quantum-mechanical calculations, this process was referred to as *geometry optimization*, a term synonymous in everyday use with *energy minimization* (which is the term this book will generally use).

The problem of minimization of a numerical function has been widely studied, for it is a special case of the general problem of optimization. One class of methods has been developed for situations in which only the value of the function (in this context, the energy), and not its derivatives, can be computed. By conducting searches near the current location in conformational space, it is possible to find a direction in which the energy decreases. The system is moved in this direction and the searching continues until a minimum is reached. Other methods rely on the ability to calculate either analytical or numerical derivatives of the energy function; these can be used in a variety of algorithms that have differing degrees of effectiveness and efficiency.

To illustrate the general idea, we first show how the analytical derivatives of typical empirical conformational energy functions are obtained, and then discuss the common minimization algorithms. The derivatives are computed almost as easily as the energy itself, and in most programs they are accumulated in the same cycle through the energy expression, Eq. (3.1), in which the energy calculation takes place.

We want to compute the first derivatives of the energy with respect to the Cartesian coordinates, namely

$$g_k = \partial E/\partial x_k \quad \text{for} \quad k = 1, 2, 3, \ldots, 3N \tag{3.7}$$

Since E is calculated as a function of the internal coordinates S_i, the Cartesian derivatives can be calculated by the chain rule:

$$g_k = \sum (\partial E/\partial S_j)(\partial S_j/\partial x_k) \tag{3.8}$$

For the bonded term, S is just the Cartesian distance metric of Eq. (3.2). For a given bond, there are only six derivative contributions, arising from the x, y, and z coordinates associated with the two atoms that form the bond.

The bond angles are somewhat more complicated because the value of the angle is computed from the dot product of two bond vectors; there are contributions to the derivatives with respect to nine coordinates (x, y, and z of the three component atoms). The torsion angles are still more involved, but once the algebra is written out and programmed the task is straightforward. In both angular cases, the chain rule (Eq. 3.8) is used to differentiate first with respect to the cosine of the angle involved, since the cosine is what is actually calculated from Cartesian coordinate algebra. Nonbonded terms are simpler, since they depend only on various inverse powers of the interatomic separation.

Second derivatives are calculated by extensions of these procedures; for bond angles and torsion angles the algebra is lengthy and tedious, but needs to be written and programmed only once. For a molecule of N atoms, the matrix of second derivatives will have $3N \times 3N$ entries; actually only slightly more than half of these have to be computed because the matrix is symmetric, i.e., $F_{ij} = F_{ji}$.

3.2.2.1 First Derivative Minimization Methods

The simplest minimization method uses the first derivatives, which measure the slope of the potential surface in the $3N$-dimensional space, to move in the direction in which the energy drops most steeply. This accounts for its name, the method of steepest descents [49]. The algorithm specifies the displacement or step Δx_i for each Cartesian component to be proportional in size to the magnitude of the gradient but opposite the direction of rise; that is,

$$\Delta x_i = -(\text{STEP})(g_i/g_{\text{rms}}) \quad \text{for} \quad i = 1, 2, 3, \ldots, 3N \tag{3.9}$$

Here STEP is a stepsize parameter that is started off at some fairly small value such as 0.005 Å, g_i is the derivative of the total energy with respect to Cartesian component i, summed up from all internal coordinates involving the atom in which component i is located, and g_{rms} is the root-mean-square gradient for the whole system,

$$g_{\text{rms}} = (\sum g_i^2)^{1/2} \tag{3.10}$$

After the displacements have been applied to all Cartesian components, the energy and gradient are calculated again. A simple algorithm is to alter the stepsize based on what happened in the last step; if the energy decreased, STEP is enlarged by, say, 20%; otherwise, STEP is cut in half. The typical behavior of this minimization method is that the energy first drops rapidly, and STEP grows, until one iteration results in overshooting the minimum. As the minimum is approached, the gradient gets smaller (by definition it is zero at the minimum). Overshooting becomes more common, and the stepsize becomes very small, so that the coordinate shifts are near zero and the conformation ceases to change appreciably. The behavior is sketched in Fig. 3.6.

The steepest descent method is rapid and simple, and it is also quite stable even when the starting conformation has a poor geometry and thus a high energy and very large derivative components. It is very good at refining the structure when it is far from a minimum, but becomes less effective when the rms gradient becomes small. The steepest descent method has no "memory" of the path the system has taken;

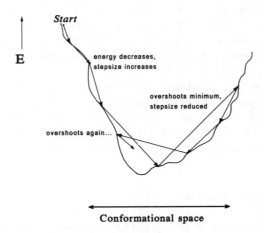

Figure 3.6. Progress of a steepest descent minimization.

each step involves only the present value of the gradients and a knowledge of whether the last step raised or lowered the energy.

More sophisticated first-derivative methods use some or all of the minimization history to accumulate more information about the nature of the potential surface in the region of the minimum toward which the system is being refined. Such methods include the conjugate gradient, Powell, and BFGS algorithms; see Ref. [23] for descriptions and references. Some of these evaluate the energy more than once before taking a step; in physical terms, the algorithms are trying out several directions and learning more about the potential surface. Consequently, they take longer to run, but are capable of finding the minimum with more precision. Some, however, are unstable when the structure has large initial gradients. What is sometimes done is to run a number of steepest descent cycles to smooth out these large initial strains, then switch to the more sophisticated first-derivative methods.

3.2.2.2 Second Derivative Minimization Methods

More time-consuming, but still more effective, are methods that use the additional information contained in the second derivatives. In physical terms, a first derivative gives the slope, or rate of change of the energy along a certain coordinate. The diagonal elements $\partial^2 E/\partial x_i^2$ of the second derivative matrix give the curvature, or rate of change of the slope as one coordinate x_i varies, and the off-diagonal elements $\partial^2 E/\partial x_i \partial x_j$ show how the slope along one coordinate varies as a different coordinate changes. In the case of a function dependent on a single variable, $y = f(x)$, the use of the curvature to find a nearby minimum is the basis of Newton's method.

Second-derivative methods are difficult to apply to large molecules because they require partial or full calculation and manipulation of the $3N \times 3N$ second-derivative matrix. One method, the Newton-Raphson algorithm, involves diagonalizing this large matrix and then finding the optimum step along each eigenvector. These calculations make use of much more information about the molecular potential, and are capable of producing accurate minima, but they are time-consuming. Modified versions also exist in which only the near-diagonal second derivative components are used; usually these include many of the largest components and give many of the benefits of the full second derivative methods with much less computing. Again the reader is referred to Ref. [23] for more details about the method.

3.2.2.3 Minimization Criteria and Effort

With numerical methods, the exact minimum is never established (except in idealized cases), so the minimization process must be terminated when certain tolerances are met. Measures that can be used to limit the process include the energy difference from step to step, the rms gradient, or the rms coordinate shift. For very large systems, it may be necessary simply to place a limit on the number of minimization steps performed; many hours of computer time will still be needed to obtain reasonably converged minima.

For small molecules, common protocols are to run several hundred steps of conjugate gradient minimization or some dozens of steps using second-derivative methods. Since energy and derivative evaluations often take only a second (and sometimes much less) for small molecules, only a few minutes are required to obtain an accurate minimum. Second derivative methods may require one or two orders of magnitude more time than first-derivative algorithms, but can produce very precise minima without a great expenditure of time. Tolerances might be set at 0.1 kcal/mol or less for convergence of the energy, with rms gradients of less than 0.01 kcal/mol-Å. For larger molecules, the convergence criteria must be weighed against the time it would take to reach them.

3.2.3   Mapping Energy Barriers and Surfaces

Once a molecule has been brought to a local minimum of its potential energy, the question arises about whether there are alternative minima. Often it is apparent from looking at the structure how to find some other minima, for example, rotation by 120° and 240° about single bonds should result in a rotational isomer, unless there is obvious steric hindrance. It is a simple matter to rotate one part of a molecule about a single bond, and then to re-minimize the energy to seek the new local minimum. If another minimum is found, then one may wish to determine the torsional energy barrier between them. If more than one variable is involved, it may be of interest to produce an energy surface.

If a molecule is sufficiently complex, it may not be obvious whether there are other minima, how many there are, or how they can be reached from the current conformation. Searching for alternative conformations is the subject of conformational search, which is introduced in the next section. Here we outline different methods for mapping out barriers and surfaces when it is obvious that there are multiple minima and we know how to generate them by making internal rotations about bonds, starting from a given conformation.

The simplest way to map out a torsional barrier is simply to rotate part of the molecule about the central bond by a small step, say 10°, re-compute the energy, and continue until as much of the curve as desired is mapped out (see Fig. 3.7). With a 10° increment, mapping of the complete torsional range would require 36 evaluations of the energy. This process is sometimes called a *rigid rotation*, because all other degrees of freedom are kept fixed at the values they had in the starting conformation. It is also called *torsional driving* since the independent variable in the process is a torsion angle.

Perhaps a more realistic method is to increment the torsion angle under study, and then re-minimize the energy of the molecule subject to the *constraint* that the torsion in question should remain fixed at the new value. That is, the minimization is with respect to all *other* internal coordinates. A simple way to do this is to add to the energy expression the constraint function $K_{cons}(V - V_{cons})^2$, where K_{cons} is large

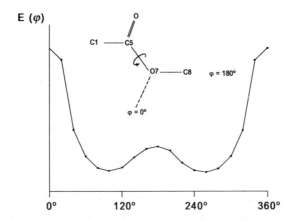

Figure 3.7. Map of torsional barrier for φ (C1—C5—O7—C8) in methyl acetate.

and V_{cons} is the value to which the internal coordinate V is to be constrained. The energy contributions from the constraint potential are ignored, but its derivatives serve to hold the coordinate near its desired value. This method is known as *flexible-geometry* or *adiabatic* mapping, for as the coordinate V moves along its path, any steric hindrances that may occur are given a chance to relax. Using the example of methyl acetate in Fig. 3.7, as rotations are carried out about the C5—O7 bond, the hydrogens on C1 may make very short nonbonded contacts with those on C8. These would lead to high energies, which could be greatly reduced by a few cycles of minimization in which the two methyl groups would undergo rotations and slight distortions that allow them to articulate. Also, the skeletal bond angles C1—C5—O7 and C5—O7—C8, as well as bond angles involving the methyl hydrogens, could open by a few degrees to relieve steric hindrance [50].

Similar processes can be carried out with two variables to produce a potential energy *surface*; most commonly, the two variables are torsion angles. A simple case to illustrate the map obtained would be the smallest hydrocarbon with two torsions, namely, propane. Each torsion would be expected to give rise to three rotational isomers: one *trans* (*t*) and two *gauche* (g^+ and g^-). The energy surface would have nine minima, which would be denoted by pairs, such as *tt*, tg^+, g^+g^-, etc. It should be noted that to map this surface with 10° increments in both variables would require computations at $36 \times 36 = 1296$ geometries. In the rigid-mapping case this means 1296 energy *evaluations*; in the flexible-geometry method it means 1296 energy *minimizations*. Under the conservative assumption of 100 iterations per minimization, the flexible map would take 100 times longer to compute; for a small molecule, the corresponding elapsed times to compute the energy surface might be 2 and 200 minutes.

One might want to evaluate a path between two conformations on an energy surface, where more than one internal coordinate changes along the path. One example would be the transition from the *tt* state of propane to the g^-g^- state, which would be a sort of diagonal along the surface. Another would be a reaction path in which a proton might be transferred from one species to another. One way to do this is to impose the path by placing constraints on two or more variables involved, with re-minimization of the energy (i.e., flexible-geometry mapping) at a selected set of increments along the path. This requires some estimate or knowledge of the transition path, which may be simple for small molecules, but impossible to predict in larger systems with many degrees of freedom.

3.2.4   Conformational Searching

As mentioned in the previous section, it may be impossible to enumerate all the local minima for a molecule. This is particularly true when more than a small number of internal coordinates can be varied. Then one must have recourse to algorithms which search, either systematically or otherwise, for other minima. The process of generating and testing alternative conformations, or *conformational search*, has received much study. Here we outline a few methods and refer the interested reader to the literature for additional information [51–54].

As indicated, the variables involved in conformational searching are the torsion angles. We have seen that the systematic coverage of torsion angle space involves a combinatorial explosion: if the range of each torsion is divided into N points, then the systematic search over M torsions generates N^M conformations (recall the above case of two torsions with 36 points each: the number of points to evaluate was 36^2). Furthermore, simply evaluating the energy of each of these conformations may not be sufficient: one may wish to carry out some cycles of energy minimization to see whether a given generated conformation leads to a new minimum or to a previously recorded one.

Torsion angles are also the "natural" variables to consider because they allow bond lengths and angles to be kept fixed. Attempts to search conformational space by random displacements of the atomic Cartesian coordinates would result in bond stretching or compression, and bond angle opening or closing, which are very "expensive" energetically because the bond and angle parameters are so relatively large. Bond lengths and angles for a given molecule do differ from one local minimum to another, but the changes are relatively small compared to the torsional changes involved.

Two phenomena complicate the conformational searching problem: the first is the combinatorial explosion mentioned above, which makes it difficult to cover all of the available conformational space; the second is the fact that the rigid-mapping technique creates conformations that have artificially high steric hindrance. This steric crowding is generally rapidly relieved, as discussed in the methyl acetate example, by just the first few cycles of energy minimization, which produce slight opening of bond angles, articulation of methyl groups, and other motions that have little effect on the overall conformation. Thus a crowded, folded conformation that starts with high energy due to a few short nonbonded contacts could minimize to a highly folded but stable local minimum. This minimum would be missed if the search process were restricted to rigid rotations.

Therefore research in conformational searching has been directed at efficiently generating random conformations that cover conformational space uniformly (rather than concentrating only on the low-energy portions), and also at rapidly evaluating whether a generated conformation really is a new local minimum.

3.2.5   Vibrational Analysis

A straightforward application of energy-function calculations is the determination of molecular vibrational modes. A molecule of N atoms has $3N - 6$ normal modes, each with a corresponding frequency and a characterization of the vibrational motion in terms of internal coordinate deformations (e.g., C—H stretch, C—C—O bend, etc.).

Once the molecule has been brought to a local minimum, one further pass through the energy calculation is performed in order to evaluate the matrix of mass-weighted second derivatives. The second derivatives represent curvatures of the energy surface along various coordinates, and are thus related to the force constants for the restoring forces that localize the molecule to that region of conformational space. The reader is referred to the book by Wilson, Decius, and Cross [36] for the mathematical details of how the matrix is formed, solved, and projected back onto the internal coordinates.

Vibrational analysis provides proof that a conformation is really a local minimum and not a saddle point; at the same time, it indicates the numerical precision of the local minimum. At a local minimum, the six lowest frequencies (which correspond to translation and rotation of the molecule as a whole) should be zero to high accuracy, and all others should be positive. At a saddle point, one or more of the six lowest frequencies will be imaginary, indicating that there is no restoring force along that normal mode. The number of imaginary frequencies indicates what type of a saddle point it is.

3.2.6   Molecular Dynamics

The concept of the classical dynamics of a molecule is simple, but its implementation can be very complicated. We will set forth the basic nature of molecular dynamics calculations, and indicate where the operational complexities arise. For further information on the details of various methods, the reader is referred to the dynamics references of Chapter 1 [20–23].

Classical dynamics is an application of the Newtonian mechanics of a system of particles acting under a force law. For any particle in motion with a given momentum, the effect of a net force on that particle is to change the momentum, i.e.,

$$F = dp/dt \tag{3.11}$$

where the momentum $p = mv$ (mass times velocity), so that $F = ma$ where m is the mass and $a = dv/dt$ is the acceleration of the particle. The force on a particle in a classical system is calculated from the force law that governs the system. In the case of planetary dynamics, for instance, the force law is the inverse-square gravitational attraction between two bodies; it is a two-body, central force. Given the positions and velocities of all the planets and other celestial bodies at a moment in time, it is possible to calculate the future evolution of the system as a set of planetary trajectories.

The situation is analogous for molecular dynamics, but the force law is somewhat more complicated. It has two-body central force terms, but they do not follow the inverse-square law; rather, they express the forces for bond stretching/compression and for nonbonded interactions. There are also three-body terms (for the bond angles) and four-body terms (for the torsion angles). Nevertheless, one can compute the instantaneous force on any atom: it is just the negative of the gradient, i.e.,

$$F_i = -g_i = -\partial E/\partial x_i \quad \text{for} \quad i = 1, 2, 3, \ldots, 3N \qquad (3.12)$$

In both planetary and molecular dynamics, one uses the instantaneous positions and forces to integrate the equations of motion using numerical prescriptions. In simple terms, the forces are assumed to remain constant for a very short time interval. The displacements and changes in velocity that will take place in that interval due to those forces are calculated and applied to the current positions and velocities of all the atoms. The process is repeated for as long as desired to build up a trajectory for the system.

It is worth noting just how small the time step must be. As a rule of thumb, it needs to be at least an order of magnitude smaller than the shortest periodic motion in the system. These are the stretching vibrations involving hydrogens (C—H stretch, N—H stretch, etc.), which have an energy of about $3500 \, \text{cm}^{-1}$. In frequency terms this is approximately $10^{14} \, \text{sec}^{-1}$. Thus the stepsize must be no larger than 10^{-15} seconds, or one femtosecond (fs). The consequence of this is that a calculation of a thousand steps simulates only one picosecond (10^{-12} sec, or 1 ps) of real time; a calculation of a million steps simulates one nanosecond (10^{-9} sec, or 1 ns). It is sobering to realize that if we can compute one dynamics step per second (and this is an optimistic figure for a molecular system of any significant size), the 1 ns simulation will take almost 278 hours — nearly 12 days — of computer time. For an isolated small organic molecule, where the calculation might go 100 times faster, it is still a 3-hour calculation. For a large polymer model, it could be considerably slower; see, for example, the calculated times for the large-scale simulations mentioned in Chapter 1 (Refs. [24–26]). Shorter simulations, say less than 100 psec in duration, can be useful for gaining an understanding of fundamental physical processes, but most physical phenomena that we can measure occur on a time scale at least as long as nanoseconds. Considerable effort has been directed toward finding ways to surmount this obstacle.

In practice, a number of details must be attended to more carefully. First, there is the question of initial conditions. If we begin with a structure that has not been energy minimized, it will in general contain localized strains. As the dynamics procedure starts, these strains will generate large displacements during the early time intervals, which represent large velocities and hence large kinetic energies. That is, the molecule will have "hot spots" rather than a uniform energy distribution. Over time, the hot spots will equilibrate with the rest of the molecule, but the time required may be undesirably long. In severe cases these hot spots can cause a simulation to produce unphysical behavior or fail due to numerical instabilities.

Alternatively, one can begin with an energy-minimized structure. Then the potential energy of the system is very small, and when the dynamics starts, the atoms will hardly move; in effect, the molecule is at a very low temperature. To obtain motions of interest, it is necessary to scale up the velocities, or to "inject" energy, so that the system's energy corresponds to an interesting temperature, such as room temperature. Again, these procedures must produce a uniform energy distribution.

One measure of the validity of a dynamics simulation is the constancy of the temperature of the system. Variations or systematic trends indicate problems or sources of error; these may require using a shorter integration step or making more subtle changes.

3.2.7   Forms of Molecular Dynamics

This introduction to molecular dynamics has indicated the general principles involved in simulating the time evolution of a molecular system. In some calculations, an isolated molecule or group of molecules is treated exactly as outlined, and that constitutes the desired simulation procedure. Sometimes, however, it is desirable to take other physical effects into account. Here we give simple descriptions of a few of them.

3.2.7.1 Periodic Boundary Conditions

Although simulation time rises with the size of the system, there is concern that using too small a system introduces edge-effects and does not really give a faithful account of bulk materials. A method of generating a semi-infinite extent of material is to create a representative portion of a system and then replicate it periodically in all directions in space, as sketched in Fig. 3.8. The central "unit cell" (which need not be at all related to a crystallographic unit cell, but serves a similar purpose as the prototype of the whole system) may have a simple cubic or a more complicated geometry, with corresponding symmetry operations used to generate copies, or images, of the cell and the atoms within it. The simulation is carried out on the central cell, with each image atom undergoing the same motions as its corresponding atom in the simulation cell. Long-range interactions between cells produce the effect of a bulk material, without the need to simulate all the particles explicitly. The particle number and density are conserved by arranging to have an image atom entering a cell whenever one leaves through the opposite face.

This technique is used very often in polymer simulations, where the entangled networks of molecules are of more interest than the behavior of a single chain isolated in space. There are some technical considerations; for example, the method introduces a periodicity into the system that could have unforeseen effects. The cells are

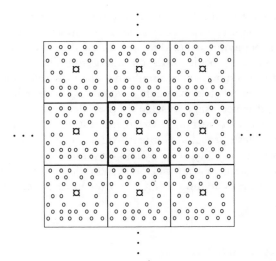

Figure 3.8. Periodic boundary conditions. The central cell and its contents are replicated in all directions in space.

correlated, in that all motions are replicated in the image cells; also, a density fluctuation (sound wave) or other effect can propagate across the simulation cell in a relatively short time, so that long-time behavior of the system may be compromised. We will not go further into the technical discussion, but rather refer the reader to the literature cited earlier in this section.

3.2.7.2 Langevin Dynamics

In some simulations the motions of certain particles or groups of atoms are of most interest, while the details of the rest of the system are less interesting. We may be interested, for example, in the motion of a solute molecule. The details of the solvent molecules may not be of interest, but we must represent their effects in any simulation of the system. A way of suppressing unwanted details while still taking into account their effect on the rest of the system is to introduce model or averaged interactions. One method for doing this is to assume that the surroundings, though not represented explicitly, exert a dissipative or drag force proportional to the velocity of each simulated particle i. Then the ideal Newtonian form $F_i = m_i a_i$ becomes

$$F_i = m_i a_i - \beta m_i v_i \tag{3.13}$$

where β is the drag or friction coefficient.

This friction, however, causes the system's energy to drop, as atoms slow down in response to the velocity-dependent drag term. If the simulation is long enough, the system will "run down" to a low temperature, just as a pendulum swinging in air will eventually come to rest as air resistance reduces its amplitude on each swing.

If constant-temperature simulations are intended, energy will have to be continually fed into the system.

3.2.7.3   Stochastic Boundary Conditions

Related both to the concerns of large systems and to the question of thermal equilibrium is the method of stochastic boundary conditions. The procedure here is to partition the system into a central region of interest, a boundary zone, and a surrounding region; see, for example, Fig. 8 of Ref. [23]. The central region is treated with ordinary molecular dynamics; the two outer zones are modeled more approximately. In the outermost region the atoms are fixed; they contribute nonbonded interactions to the central region but the forces on them are ignored and they are not moved during the simulation. In the boundary layer, the atoms are subjected to stochastic forces. These random fluctuations of kinetic energy cause the boundary zone to act as both an energy sink and an energy source for the simulated atoms in the central region.

The stochastic boundary approach is most appropriate for studying relatively rapid events localized within a set of surroundings. The ideal example, for which the approach was developed, is an enzyme-ligand interaction (which may be reactive or not), in which the enzyme's active site or binding site is the center of the region of detailed simulation, and atoms more than a few ångstroms distant can be treated as "spectators." As in the periodic boundary approach, the small size of the simulation region may introduce technical difficulties having to do with long-time behavior.

3.2.7.4   Brownian Dynamics

In macromolecular dynamics, the detailed motions of small portions of the system may not be of much interest, because the phenomena of interest depend on large group motions or whole-molecule tumbling or diffusion. This emphasis is especially appropriate in polymer studies, where some mechanical and rheological properties, for instance, are determined by slow processes involving the slippage of large portions of macromolecular chains past one another. The details of how chemical functional groups affect such relaxation is valuable, and may be the subject of ordinary molecular dynamics studies; the information learned can then be used to devise approximate interactions that can be applied to larger pieces. A polymer chain might be represented as a collection of jointed rods or even as a large ellipsoidal particle.

The basic approach of Brownian dynamics is to consider the molecular motions as diffusion-controlled. The diffusion coefficient enters directly into the equations of motion and controls the rates of displacement of the units of the system, which may be atoms, groups of atoms, or model entities that simplify the representation of the macromolecules. With these techniques it is possible to simulate time evolutions up into the picosecond range, or at least three orders of magnitude greater than the duration of full molecular dynamics simulations. Naturally a different level of detail is present in the results, and each type of simulation has to be interpreted appropriately.

3.2.7.5 Dynamics with Two Time Scales

Since one barrier to running longer simulations is the short time step necessitated by the fast motions of a system, an avenue of research has been to devise ways to separate out these fast motions and allow longer simulations of the slower motions. One method is to simplify the representation of the molecule, as indicated in the above paragraphs. Another is to consider a separation of variables such that slower motions are simulated with a coarser time step. Some of these two-time-scale treatments have resulted in significant improvements in the ratio of time simulated to the real time spent calculating the motions [55].

3.2.8   Applications of Molecular Dynamics

While the reason for development of the molecular dynamics technique was to simulate the time evolution of molecular systems, there are several ways in which this can be used. We can think of the "normal" or ordinary molecular dynamics simulation as one in which the molecule or system is first energy minimized, then slowly heated and equilibrated through a preliminary simulation, and then allowed to evolve at a constant model temperature for a period of time sufficient to exhibit the behavior of interest. Here we present three additional ways in which molecular dynamics has been used.

3.2.8.1 Conformational Searching

Since the molecule or system is not static during a simulation, molecular dynamics offers one method of conformational searching. As thermal energy is introduced into the system, and as it flows back and forth between various degrees of freedom, the molecule explores the potential energy surface in the neighborhood of the local minimum from which it starts. The simulation temperature, the rigidity of the internal degrees of freedom, and the duration of the simulation determine how much conformational space will be traversed. Regions bounded by high barriers, or which have narrow minima, will be unlikely to be visited. If the simulation temperature is high, the molecule may "fly" over such regions without being able to disperse enough energy to spend time in that region of conformational space.

There are both advantages and drawbacks to using molecular dynamics as a search method. An advantage is that every conformation generated by a simulation is a realistic one, obtained by a sequence of steps that rigorously follows from classical mechanics. But the corresponding disadvantage is that the system cannot move arbitrarily far from its starting location in a simulation of a given duration. Further, because of the problems mentioned in the previous paragraph, dynamics may be very inefficient at generating some conformations. It may instead give a very complete picture of the potential energy surface in a small region near the starting point.

3.2.8.2 Simulated Annealing

The presence of temperature, or of kinetic energy, in molecular dynamics can be usefully employed to foster conformational changes. As in conformational searching, increased simulation temperature allows the molecule to move over potential barriers and to explore larger areas of conformational space. In simulated annealing, the system is deliberately heated to a high temperature (1000 K or more) to permit it to sample alternate conformations. The hot system is cooled slowly, or *annealed*, by gradually removing kinetic energy from the dynamic simulation. Essential components of the technique are the heating and cooling schedules and also certain conformational restraints that are applied to maintain structural integrity at high temperatures. Examples of restraints include constraint potentials to prevent racemization through inversion of chiral centers, or to keep aromatic rings flat.

   As its name implies, simulated annealing is a means of removing residual strains in a structure by allowing it to "melt" or become more fluid internally, then slowly cooling it back to its starting temperature. This is the equivalent, in molecular simulations, of the physical process of annealing metals or other materials to obtain a finished product with smaller crystals or a more uniform composition. In both processes, the purpose is to produce a more stable structure whose internal energy is lower because its internal strains have had an opportunity to undergo relaxation.

3.2.8.3 Quenched Dynamics

As an alternative to simulated annealing, simulated quenching entails a rapid drop in temperature to "freeze" the system. Slow heating is carried out by the usual method of injecting kinetic energy, namely periodically scaling up the velocities of the particles in the system. As the dynamics proceeds at the elevated temperature, conformations ("snapshots") are saved at regular intervals. In contrast to simulated annealing, the saved conformations are not cooled slowly through molecular dynamics, but rather "frozen" abruptly by energy minimization. The minimized conformations are then analyzed and compared to determine whether new conformations have resulted. Thus quenched dynamics, like simulated annealing, can be used for purposes similar to conformational searching. The differences among the methods are in how the heating and cooling are achieved, how long the simulations are run, and whether any restraining potentials are needed.

3.3   Summary

All the molecular mechanics and molecular dynamics operations carried out with empirical force fields follow logically from the basic process of evaluating the energy and its derivatives by systematically adding contributions from every internal coordinate and nonbonded interaction defined for the molecule or molecular system. To begin the Chapter we enumerated these interactions in detail for a small organic molecule; the process is the same in principle for larger molecules and for systems consisting of multiple molecules. The conventions for defining internal coordinates must be consistently applied to assure transferability of the force field; for example, if all possible torsions about a single bond are defined in one system, then the same thing must be done for analogous systems. Besides the complete list of interactions, two further ingredients are needed before calculations can begin: a starting conformation specifying the Cartesian coordinates of every atom in the system, and the table of energy parameters for every interaction type present in the system. The energy calculation then processes each interaction, using the atoms forming it, and their coordinates, to obtain the present value of the internal coordinate, and adding in the energy contribution. With some additional coordinate geometry, the energy derivative contributions are accumulated during the same cycle through the interaction list. Further operations — energy minimization, mapping of energy barriers and surfaces (either with rigid geometry or with the geometry re-minimized at each point with respect to all other coordinates), conformational search, vibrational analysis, and molecular dynamics — follow in a straightforward manner from the basic energy calculation. These essential elements of molecular modeling technique will reappear throughout this book.

4

Building Models of Polymeric Systems

This book began with a general description of the rationale for scientific modeling and the desirable characteristics of a model. One of the elements that makes a good model is the ease with which it can be set up or altered; another is the carefully thought out compromise between simplicity of evaluation and fidelity to the physical principles involved. Model building is the first step in any calculation or simulation; no matter how accurate the model is, or how convenient it may be to extract quantities or properties, it must first be built and specified as input to the calculation. Therefore in this chapter we explore in some detail the subject of model building with reference to polymer systems.

While the computational requirements of simulations are often of foremost concern in the mind of the investigator, it should be recognized that creating the model can be time-consuming and computation-intensive in itself. Often, the main issue in polymeric systems is the disorder or randomness of the system. Polymer modeling cannot begin from the same premise as protein modeling, in which there is one representative structure, such as the crystal structure determined by X-ray diffraction techniques, that characterizes a "typical" molecule. Polymers instead have a distribution of lengths, forms of isomerization, and three-dimensional arrangements. Fig. 1.2 gives a schematic view of the situation. To make a realistic material model, it is necessary somehow to reproduce these facts in the model, and to do it in a manner characteristic of the real substance we wish to study. This means that building a polymer model requires more, sometimes much more, work than constructing a protein molecule.

Further, initial conditions of a model can influence the results obtained. Unintended symmetries and regularities can make the results irrelevant to real systems or cause artifacts in the simulated behavior. Randomization, removal of initial strains, and correct equilibration of the starting model are important and may require significant computation to achieve.

The process of building an atomistic model of a polymeric system can be considered at four levels: the monomer, the single polymer chain, the material aggregation of multiple chains, and the addition of any foreign agents, typically solvent or other small molecules. In practice, the scientist may not need to specify all four steps, as some information may be provided by the software used; however, we will follow this sequence in order to illustrate the considerations of model building at all levels of detail.

4.1   Defining Monomers

In Chapter 3 we have seen the detailed nature of the information required to define a small organic molecule and prepare the corresponding coding for input to a computational modeling program. Monomers used to build polymeric substances need to be specified equally meticulously. The only elaboration not covered in Chapter 3 was the detail of making the definitions in such a way that different monomers can be linked together successively, with all the information being accumulated to produce the complete input for a polymer chain. The basic technique used is to consider the atom sequence numbers as *relative*, rather than absolute, numbers; see Fig. 4.1. This allows the monomer to be added onto a previously grown and defined chain consisting of N atoms; then the first atom of the newly added monomer is not atom 1, but atom $N + 1$; atom 2 of the monomer becomes atom $N + 2$ of the growing chain; and so on. The internal coordinate definitions need to be set up according to conventions such that those which cross the junction from the previously grown part to the new monomer (such as the bond from atom N to atom $N + 1$) are correctly specified.

Commercial software packages contain libraries of pre-defined monomers which are set up so that the operator only has to specify the monomer sequence to get a complete definition of a polymer chain. The methods were first developed for protein modeling, where the monomers are the 20 naturally occurring amino acids [56]. Polymer libraries need to be much larger than this, because there are many more

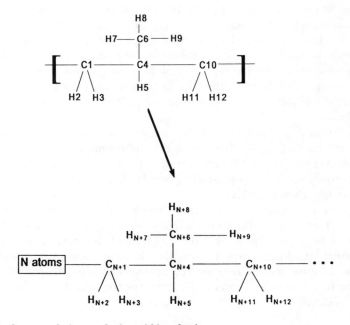

Figure 4.1. Absolute *vs.* relative numbering within subunits.

monomers in common use, and they also must provide a way for the user to specify
new, perhaps proprietary monomers, and add them into the libraries.

Branching and isomerization may also be provided for at the monomer level.
Each monomer entry must be made up with an attachment point and a continuation
point in mind. Thus, if it is possible for a monomer to add on to the growing polymer
in more than one way, or if a monomer is to be defined as a branch point, a separate
entry in the monomer library is needed; see Fig. 4.2 for two examples. In effect, the
differently bonded monomer is treated as a new, separately defined monomer. Isomers
can be accounted for in a similar fashion. Structural isomers, such as the pair shown
in Fig. 4.3, have different chemical connectivity, and this difference must be reflected
in their input files. But chiral pairs, such as *D*- and *L*-amino acids, have identical
connectivity and both members of the pair can be represented by a single entry. For
this case, the distinction is not made until an initial geometry is assigned.

Definition of connectivity (internal coordinate lists) is formally separate from
generation of geometry (Cartesian coordinates). The internal coordinate lists are
created by one "pass" through the monomer sequence, as described in the following
section. For any structure thus defined, it is possible to generate many different
coordinate sets, corresponding to different spatial arrangements of the polymer chain.
Most often, this is done by using coordinate templates that define the internal
geometry of each monomer in some standard conformation. Bond lengths and bond
angles are set to standard or reasonable values, and the torsions are also fixed in
standard ways (such as all-*trans*). As each monomer is added to the growing polymer

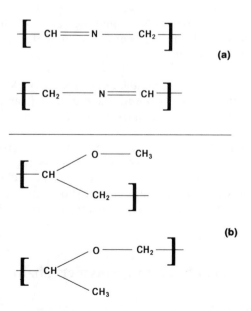

Figure 4.2. Monomers which add to the growing polymer in different fashions need to be defined separately
in the monomer library. (a), head-to-tail isomerism; (b), different continuation points.

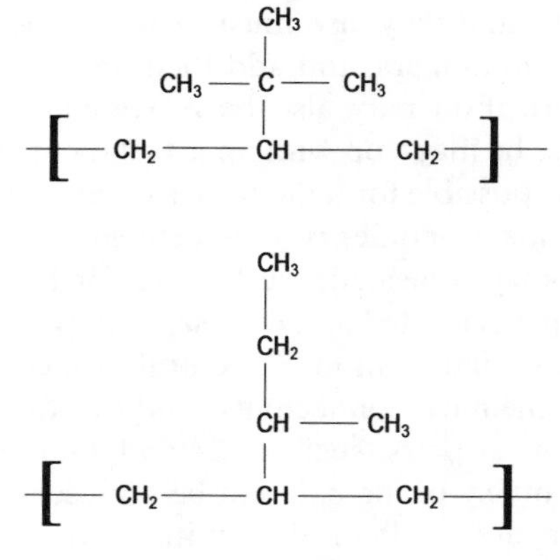

$$CH_3$$
$$|$$
$$CH_3 - C - CH_3$$
$$|$$
$$\left[- CH_2 - CH - CH_2 - \right]$$

$$CH_3$$
$$|$$
$$CH_2$$
$$|$$
$$CH - CH_3$$
$$|$$
$$\left[- CH_2 - CH - CH_2 - \right]$$

Figure 4.3. Chemical isomers, though identical in chemical formula, have different connectivities and must be defined separately in the monomer library.

chain, the coordinate template is translated and rotated to the proper orientation for attachment, then the torsion angles are modified to the desired values.

It is certainly true that bond lengths and angles should vary slightly, depending on the local situation of each residue, but as a first approximation, and as a simplification in geometry generation, they can be regarded as fixed, with only the torsion angles as the degrees of freedom which specify the chain geometry. Later, when the system is subjected to energy minimization, the template values will change in accordance with the local forces. The magnitudes of these changes can be seen from a study [57] in which 2,4-diphenylpentane, a model for a styrene dimer, was geometry-optimized with an *ab initio* treatment for a range of main chain torsion angles. Crowding of the phenyl sidegroups caused variations of up to several hundredths of an ångstrom unit for bondlengths, and up to 8.6° for bond angles. For most chain generation work, however, standardized template geometries are sufficient to build the chain; energy minimization will introduce the realistic variations discussed.

As a final note on monomer definitions, we note that the monomer libraries reflect the choice between all-atom and united-atom models. As the simplest example, a polyethylene unit defined with all atoms (i.e., $-CH_2-$) has $C-C-H$ and $H-C-H$ bond angles as internal coordinates, while the extended-atom analog (i.e., $-M-$ where M is the extended atom representing a methylene group) does not.

4.2   Linking Monomers to Form a Polymer Chain

The operation of selecting and linking monomers to form a single polymer chain can vary in complexity. At its simplest, it requires only specification of the (single) monomer and the degree of polymerization. If more than one monomer is present, the user can designate an explicit sequence monomer by monomer, just as would be done to create a protein with a known primary structure (amino acid sequence). It is unlikely, however, that the polymerization sequence for real polymers would be known in the first place; and if it were, it would not be consistent from chain to chain except in special cases. Therefore most software systems provide a more general set of methods to generate copolymer chains.

4.2.1 Sequence Editor

For a regularly alternating block copolymer $(AB)_n$, software model builders allow the specification of the sequence AB followed by a degree of repetition. The same facilities take care of regularly blocked copolymers of the form $(A_iB_j)_n$. The software facility involved is a relatively simple *sequence editor* which needs no knowledge of what the symbols it manipulates stand for; it simply adds and deletes, copies, duplicates, and repeats sequence codes which consist of a single character (as in genetic codes) or more. With point-and-click operations using a mouse or keyboard to identify the desired monomer codes, the length of the individual codes is unimportant (one to four characters are typical), and the length of the sequence that can be manipulated is very large.

Random copolymers are also provided. The user need only specify the percentage of A units, B units, and so on, and the sequence editor will generate a random sequence that conforms to the stated percentages. Some software operates not in absolute percentages, but in *probabilities* that a B unit will polymerize next, given that the prior unit is an A or something more complicated.

The key point is that the sequence generator is merely manipulating symbols, and need have no information about the chemical representation of the monomers. Further, shortcomings of a sequence builder can be overcome, or special requirements accommodated, by a manual sequence-editing process, or by generating the sequence file with a user-written program. The sequence generator is then instructed to read in the file, which if properly prepared should be indistinguishable from one prepared by the sequence builder itself. Fig. 4.4 summarizes the operation of the sequence builder. Note in Fig. 4.4 that the generation of a starting conformation comes *after* the operation of the sequence builder, which does not need to be aware of any geometrical details of the monomers. The same is true of the specification of the list of internal coordinates and nonbonded interactions: the monomer sequence generated by the sequence builder is used to retrieve the definition for each monomer in turn and link them together with the correct sequential atom numbering (Fig. 4.1).

Some aspects of polymer structure can be specified at this stage of model building. For example, *linear polymers* may be the default, but a branching unit might be inserted at a specific point. *Tacticity* that results from a chiral center in the monomer can be handled by defining each enantiomer as a different entry in the monomer library, and then using the sequence-manipulation techniques just covered to generate the isotactic (all sidegroups with the same orientation), syndiotactic (regularly

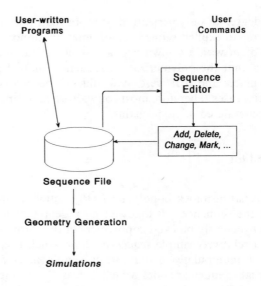

Figure 4.4. Operation of the sequence editor.

alternating), or atactic (random) form. During the sequence-generation phase tacticity only involves designation of the handedness of each monomer; the actual geometric details are not needed until an initial conformation is built.

The sequence editor, as indicated, does not deal with the details of the atomic structure. But before force-field calculations can commence, these details must be resolved. We have already indicated how the internal-coordinate definitions are put in place in the monomer library, and then linked together through a relative numbering system. The next ingredient required is a starting conformation which includes the Cartesian atomic coordinates of every atom (or equivalently, all the internal coordinates needed to calculate the Cartesian coordinates). This may not have to be assigned to each chain at the moment its sequence is specified, but it must be eventually specified for all chains in the material model before any calculation can take place. We now briefly consider ways to generate a detailed geometry for a polymer chain.

4.2.2   Helices

The simplest structure-generation rule for the homopolymer $(A)_n$ would be to assign each monomer the identical internal geometry; that is, to assign each one the same set of bond lengths, bond angles, and most importantly, main-chain torsion angles. The general structure resulting from such a prescription is a helix, because each monomer adds a fixed length to the chain and introduces a constant increment of twist. The length and twist increments are properties that depend on the details of the monomer structure and the main-chain torsion angles. A special case of a helix occurs when the main-chain torsions are all 180° (*trans*); this results in an extended, linear chain, which is a degenerate form of a helix. As the degree of twist per monomer increases, the chain spirals more tightly. Beyond a certain degree of winding, which depends on the internal geometry of the monomer, the winding becomes so tight that new added monomers must make very short nonbonded contacts with existing ones, and the internal conformational energy of the chain must be very large. There is nothing that prohibits us from specifying such an overwound chain, but if its energy is high it is unlikely to exist and its properties are unlikely to contribute to the properties of the system as a whole.

Helices are customarily specified in terms of the number of monomers p per turn q, where p and q are integers; e.g., in an 8/5 helix, eight monomers produce five turns of the helix. This is not necessarily simply related to the main-chain torsion angles. A discussion relating the two methods can be found in Ref. [58] and references therein. Fig. 4.5 shows some representative polymer helices.

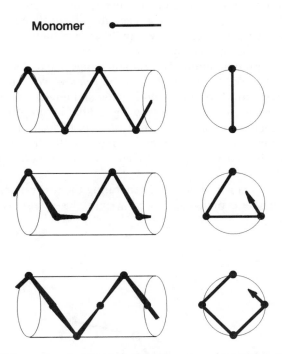

Figure 4.5. Regular helices are constructed by repetition of monomers with identical geometry. Illustrated here are forms in which an integral number of monomers make up one turn of helix. Non-integral forms also exist; an example in biopolymers is the 3_{10} helix, in which ten amino acid residues make up three turns of the helix. The ratio of monomers to turns depends on the internal geometry, valence factors at monomer junctions, and packing characteristics. *Left:* view perpendicular to helix axis; *right:* view parallel to helix axis. *Top illustration:* 2/1 helix. 2 monomers form one "turn" of this degenerate helix, which is a zig-zag or all-*trans* extended form. *Middle:* 3/1 helix. *Bottom:* 4/1 helix.

4.2.3   Chain Propagation

While regular helical structures may be important in crystalline polymers, much polymer science is concerned with amorphous polymers or mixtures that have areas with different amounts of order. It is therefore necessary to be able to create or propagate polymer chains that do not have regular or repeating geometries. A general way to do this is to specify random (or at least non-uniform) sets of main-chain torsion angles for successive monomers, and to build up the starting geometry one bond at a time. The first monomer is placed in a standard way, e.g., with the first main-chain bond along the positive x-axis; see Fig. 4.6. The first atom is at the origin of the coordinates, and the second is placed on the positive x-axis one bondlength from the first. The third atom is placed in the xz-plane; its bond distance from the second atom, and the angle it forms with the prior two atoms are required in order to calculate its coordinates. The fourth atom (and all subsequent atoms) will in general not lie in the xz-plane, and three parameters are needed to place it: the bondlength from atom 3, the valence angle formed with atoms 3 and 2; and the dihedral angle 1-2-3-4. The Cartesian coordinate geometry manipulations needed to place atoms, given the required bondlengths, valence angles, and dihedral angles, are not difficult, and long chains can be constructed very rapidly on a computer.

One method of choosing each successive set of main-chain torsion angles would be simply to generate random numbers within the range of 0 to 360°. This prescription is a close relative of a well-known one: it is the *random walk* in three dimensions, modified only by restrictions on the bond lengths and angles that must be observed when linking each new monomer to the growing chain. The simpler, standard random walk in three dimensions involves a vector, or step, of fixed length, which can be taken in any direction, without constraints arising from the direction of the previous step; this corresponds to a freely-jointed chain, whose properties have been extensively studied [8–10].

A somewhat more realistic method of generating the torsion angles is to consider their "intrinsic" energetic preferences, and weight the randomly generated value

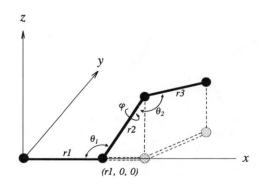

Figure 4.6. Building up atomic coordinates from internal coordinates.

accordingly. For illustration, let us assume that a *trans* torsion has the lowest energy. Other local torsional minima, such as *gauche* states, would be slightly higher in energy; and for any value of the torsion angle, the energy relative to that of the *trans* state could be computed from the empirical energy functions or from one of the more computationally intensive levels of theory. Thus the randomly generated torsion angle would be associated with a conformation whose relative energy is ΔE, and which is less probable than the *trans* conformation by the Boltzmann factor $\exp(-\Delta E/kT)$. Whether to accept this conformation is decided by the standard Metropolis Monte Carlo procedure depicted in Fig. 4.7: the conformation is kept if the Boltzmann factor is larger than a random number between zero and one. If it is not accepted, a new torsional angle and a new random number are generated, and the process is repeated until an acceptable conformation has been found; the procedure is continued for each additional torsion in the chain. Higher temperatures will increase the probability of acceptance of conformations with high ΔE. If, as assumed here, the *trans* state has the lowest conformational energy, then at low temperatures this chain-generation process will produce mostly linear, extended chains; as the temperature rises, more kinked and folded chains will be generated.

It is important to contrast the *generation of a specific instance of a polymer chain*, using the above procedure, with the *computation of average properties* using the Rotational Isomeric State (RIS) theory [60]. In RIS theory, the probability of

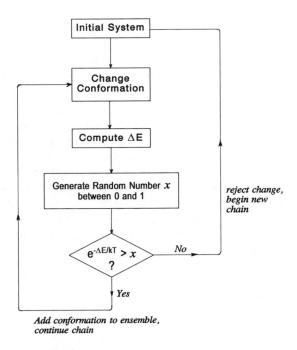

Figure 4.7. The Metropolis algorithm and creation of a Markov chain.

obtaining the various discrete torsional states is computed from an estimate of the relative energies of these states, using the Boltzmann factor $\exp(-\Delta E/kt)$. A statistical weight matrix is constructed whose elements give the probability of finding a new monomer in conformational state k if its predecessor is in state j. For a polyethylene-like main chain with *trans*, *gauche*$^+$, and *gauche*$^-$ states, a 3×3 matrix is constructed. Next this statistical weight matrix is combined with geometric and other information to produce a generator matrix. Various products and statistical expressions using the generator matrix are evaluated to obtain the configuration-dependent properties of a polymer chain of N units. These results are configurational averages characteristic of a statistical ensemble of chains. At no point in the RIS theory is any specific instance of a chain actually constructed. What we are considering in this Chapter is the building of actual models, in which every atom is assigned coordinates in space, and in which each chain represents one example of a possible configuration that could exist. Also, in the chain propagation method described in this section, torsion angles may take on any (continuous) value, mediated only by the energetic preferences of the structure. Chain propagation thus builds a structure having a distribution of torsion angles, whereas in RIS theory torsions are restricted to exact values associated with a small number of discrete states. Nevertheless, if sufficient numbers of model chains were propagated, their torsions should cluster about the discrete state values, and the configurational averages should converge to values similar to those predicted by RIS theory.

4.2.4 Self-Avoidance

In the discussion of helices we encountered the problem that a new monomer could be placed so as to make short nonbonded contacts with a previous one. The same problem arises in the chain propagation scheme just discussed; it is entirely possible that the growing chain, whether generated by regular torsion angles, randomly chosen ones, or statistically weighted ones, could double back through space and eventually intersect with an existing piece of polymer. The resulting close nonbonded contacts will produce a high-energy structure, which is highly improbable, and therefore would likely be eliminated by the Monte Carlo acceptance criterion. That is, even if the monomer conformation were acceptable in terms of the torsional energy, long-range interactions — close contacts between parts of the chain widely separated in linear sequence — would make it unfavorable. This question of *self-avoidance*, or excluded volume, has not been addressed in the models discussed so far; it must be taken into account in order to produce realistic structures. At the same time, if we wish to generate dense, amorphous structures, it is necessary to be able to create highly folded, entangled, or entwined structures, which are densely packed and whose nonbonded contacts are just acceptable. We now consider the computations and methods involved in self-avoidance.

With empirical energy function calculations it is straightforward to check the energetic situation of a newly added monomer, not only internally (i.e., as a function of torsion angles), but also with respect to the already existing chain. Nonbonded

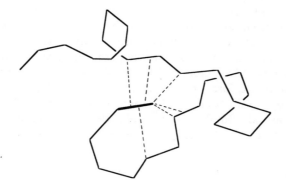

Figure 4.8. Checking the new monomer for avoidance of existing structure.

distances (or better, energies) can be calculated between the atoms of the new monomer and the existing chain (see Fig. 4.8). If there are N_m atoms in the monomer and N_c in the chain, then the number of nonbonded interactions is approximately $N_m \times N_c$. Even for fairly large monomers (say $N_m = 25$) and a large chain (say N_c = several thousand), the calculation for each new monomer is not a large one and can be done while the user waits for the result, or can conveniently be incorporated into a chain-building routine that operates in a batch mode.

The criterion for rejection of the new monomer conformation need not be extremely stringent; also it need not be an absolute numerical cutoff, but may be governed by probability, as above for torsion angle selection. It is acceptable to permit a certain amount of strain per residue during the building phase, with the understanding that this strain must be removed by an energy-minimization process once the building of the chain or set of chains is done. This energy minimization will allow all atoms in the model to shift slightly so as to relax local strains or "hot spots," as they were called earlier (Sec. 3.2.6). If the rejection criterion is stringent, there are two consequences: first, the building process will take longer to reach a certain degree of polymerization, as more rejections occur; and second, the process will be biased toward less dense, more spread out models. The larger the amount of strain permitted per monomer, the more possible it is for the model to curl back on itself or through itself to generate entanglements and other structures leading to higher density. Later in this Chapter we will review case studies showing the actual practice of these procedures.

If a new monomer must be rejected, then there are a number of prescriptions for what to do next. The simplest, of course, is just to try again with a new set of main-chain torsion angles. If after some fixed number of trials, no acceptable conformation has been generated, then the attempt may be abandoned, and the chain shortened by removing the last successfully placed monomer. The trial placements then start again. In this way the chain explores various possibilities leading to a variety of amorphous conformations. A collection of generated chains can be considered as an ensemble and treated with standard statistical procedures.

Experience (see case studies later in this Chapter) shows that it is highly unlikely to generate coiled samples at realistic densities by means of the procedure described here. One technique that leads to a higher probability of success is to use reduced van der Waals radii for all atoms, temporarily permitting abnormally close contacts; another version ignores the nonbonded forces altogether and permits overlaps. In both cases the nonbonded forces must somehow be gradually brought back to their full strength, and the strains removed by some annealing procedure making use of energy minimization and/or molecular dynamics, before the sample can be considered realistic and ready to use for further simulations.

4.3   Building a Multiple-Chain Material Model

Up to this point we have concentrated on single monomers and single polymer chains made up of a string of monomers. We next take up the considerations involved in building a detailed, realistic material model consisting of many polymer chains. The most important modeling device is *periodic boundary conditions* to simulate an infinite extent of material and avoid problems from edge effects. The special properties of interfaces and their associated edge effects have their own interest; however, in order to concentrate first on more basic modeling techniques, those topics are deferred to Chapter 7.

Periodic boundary conditions were introduced in Sec. 3.2.7 in conjunction with molecular dynamics; the basic idea is to choose a central cell and replicate it throughout space. For surface problems, the cell is reproduced in two dimensions to cover an infinite plane; to model bulk material, the cell is reproduced in three dimensions. Each atom in the central cell appears in the same relative position within every image cell.

If the chain propagation procedure is begun in the center of a periodic box, then as the chain grows and exits through one surface, it enters the box through the opposite face. Although the propagation procedure is simply extending one long, continuous chain, the periodic box appears to contain pieces of multiple chains. As far as the energy calculation is concerned, the chains are distinct, and they interact with each other through nonbonded forces. In this way the periodic boundary scheme and the chain propagation method combine to generate apparent networks of polymer chains.

The energy function calculations are carried out on the atoms of the central cell, which experience forces arising from their own covalent connections, but also experience forces arising from nonbonded interactions with the atoms in both the central cell and the image cells. Naturally the covalent connections must be properly terminated across cell boundaries, so as not to leave any half-formed bonds, bond angles, and torsion angles. As the atom shifts of the central cell are calculated during energy minimization or molecular dynamics, they are applied equally to the central-cell atoms and the image atoms. If an atom moves out of one cell, it enters the next one, and is replicated in all cells; in effect, the atom disappears through one face of the cell and reappears from the opposite face. This enforces periodicity and preserves the total number of atoms in the system. Methods also exist which permit the number of atoms to change during the simulation.

The criteria for forming the central cell are not always clear; certainly it needs to be large enough to give a representative sample of the material, but not so large that it contains a very great number of atoms. One problem that arises then is difficulty in simulating a dilute solution. This requires one solute molecule surrounded by many solvent molecules, which may in turn require too large a unit cell to be practicable. Another question concerns the effect that the periodic nature of the system has on the independence of motions within the cell. An effect starting at one edge of a cell takes a finite time to propagate across it to the next cell, which means that the effect is repeating or echoing in the original cell. Such a wave can be represented by a sound wave, whose speed in water is about 15 Å per picosecond. Thus self-effects will begin after very short times and possibly obscure the correct development of properties with longer time constants.

4.4   Case Studies of Model Building

After the foregoing discussion of techniques, we are now in a position to consider a number of studies from the literature, illustrating the methods described. Examples can be found using single and multiple chains in both crystalline and amorphous polymer models.

4.4.1   Single Chains

In Sec. 4.2.3 above, techniques for generating single chains were introduced. We noted that the use of random torsion angles, conditionally accepted based on the torsional energetics, led to a temperature-dependent geometrical preference. A practical illustration of this is seen in work described by Clarke [61]. Random copolymers of hydroxybenzoic acid (HBA) and hydroxynaphthoic acid (HNA) were generated at two temperatures, 70 and 600 K. All the model-building trials were started off in the same direction, and a graphic superposition of samples of the generated chains made it easy to see qualitatively how lower temperature favored a linear, rod-like geometry. Numerical values of the persistence length, or the mean distance covered by the chain in the direction of the first monomer unit, were also determined and gave a quantitative measure, comparable with experimental data, of the phenomenon.

In subsequent work we will see other examples of simulations based on single chains. While it may seem unlikely that a single chain could represent the properties of a complicated material in which many different kinds of polymer chains overlap and intertwine, the model is appropriate under the assumption that intra- and intermolecular excluded volume effects just cancel each other. When this is so, the intrinsic properties of the chain are the deciding factor which governs the folding. This is the case for simple polymer melts and for dilute solutions in appropriate solvents.

4.4.2   Crystalline Domains

A crystalline polymer model is clearly easier to generate than an amorphous one, since it can be built by simple replication and alignment of one or a few chains. For example, an idealized polyethylene crystal can be built by constructing a single all-*trans* chain and translating it in directions perpendicular to its length to form a bundle. Sumpter, Noid, and Wunderlich [62] created a model orthorhombic poly-ethylene crystal in this fashion starting with a single chain of 100 —CH_2— extended atoms. Up to 37 mobile chains were surrounded by a matrix of 24 fixed chains, for a total of 61 chains or 6100 atoms. They did not impose periodic boundary conditions, instead using the outer 24 fixed chains as a boundary layer (Fig. 4.9). This is slightly different from the boundary layer methodology introduced in Sec. 3.2.7.3, which was originally designed for studies of the active sites of proteins. There the spherical boundary layer surrounded the active site, and could act either as a heat sink (all atoms in the boundary layer remain fixed) or as a stochastic heat bath (the boundary layer provides random impulses that could increase or decrease the kinetic energy of atoms in the simulation zone). In this crystal simulation, the surrounding chains

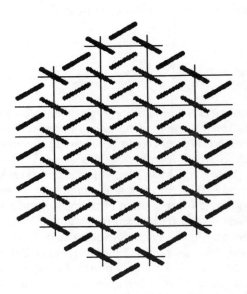

Figure 4.9. End view of the idealized polyethylene crystal model. The 37 inner chains are free to move according to the molecular dynamics simulation; the 24 chains in the outer ring are fixed in space. Reprinted with permission from Ref. 62. Copyright 1990 American Institute of Physics.

serve as a static layer, which contains the simulation region but does not interact with it.

In later work by the same group [63] a larger system consisting of 192 chains of $C_{50}H_{102}$, for a total of 9600 —CH_2— extended atoms, was constructed. In this larger crystal, no constraints were imposed — even the outer chains were free to move. As built, the system had a density of about 1 g/cm³, which is too high, even for highly crystalline polyethylene, and expansion readily took place during energy minimization and molecular dynamics. This could not have occurred if the outer chains had been fixed as in the earlier work.

Schmieg and Hägele [59] built single-chain helices of polyisobutylene and minimized the energy of the chain using semiempirical calculations. They then created arrays of chains, now keeping each individual chain fixed at the energy-minimized geometry and allowing only rigid-body motions (i.e., translations and rotations of chains) in the energy minimization of the array. From this they deduced lattice parameters for the crystals.

An infinite crystalline domain can be produced by defining a unit cell in the middle of a densely packed array, such as those used in the two examples given so far, and applying periodic boundary conditions. Some of the details involved in doing this are discussed in Ref. [58]. In particular, these authors stress the importance of considering both intermolecular (i.e., single-chain) energetics and the nonbonded interactions between different chains. The energy is minimized simultaneously with respect to both contributions, and a vibrational analysis is carried out. The properties calculated include packing parameters, energy density, and elastic constants, among others.

4.4.3   Amorphous Polymers Through Chain Propagation

In this section we review several case studies involving the basic technique of chain propagation with self-avoidance. First the dimensions of the periodic box, which is usually cubic, are chosen; then chain propagation takes place, subject to short- and long-range interactions that provide correct chain statistics (e.g., fraction of *trans* bonds). As the chain propagates out of the periodic box through one face, it enters the box through the opposite face. Replication of the box thus produces correctly covalently connected chains. The second step is the equilibration and removal of initial close contacts.

An important first application of this methodology was reported by Theodorou and Suter [64], who studied the structural properties of atactic polypropylene at −40°C. They noted the problems of chain propagation based only on rotational isomeric state probabilities and defined the method of taking into account long-range nonbonded interactions. They used a chain with degree of polymerization 76 (equivalent to 455 atoms per chain for polypropylene) in a cube 18.15 Å on each axis. Fig. 4.10 shows the appearance of the generated model. Energy minimization, or "relaxation of the model to mechanical equilibrium," was recognized as a major problem and was approached with a three-step strategy. In the first step, atomic radii

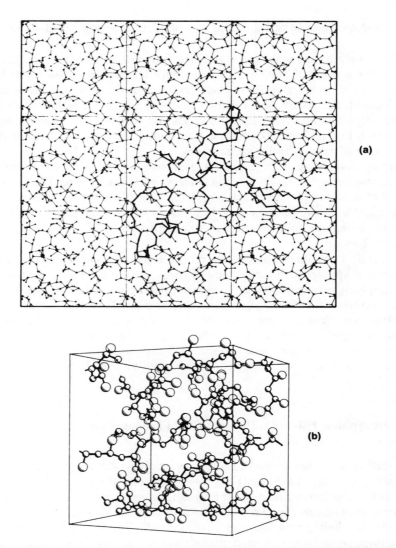

Figure 4.10. Model structure of an amorphous glassy polymer. (a) Unit cell and eight neighboring images, projected onto a plane; (b) three-dimensional drawing of the energy-minimized central unit cell. Reprinted with permission from Ref. 64. Copyright 1985 American Chemical Society.

were kept at half their actual size, the nonbonded potentials were modified to be softer than normal and to have no attractive part, and rotation barriers were ignored. In the second step the radii were increased to actual size and the full rotation barriers were added; while the third step was a minimization with the full nonbonded potentials, radii of actual size, and full torsional potentials. Details and progress of the minimization are given in the paper. The fifteen model structures generated by repeated applications of these procedures served as the ensemble for evaluation of structural properties.

Another group under the direction of Suter [65] applied a similar approach to the study of glassy Bisphenol A polycarbonate, which has a larger and more complicated repeat unit with six single bonds about which rotation can occur. This flexibility created problems in structure generation, which were resolved by treating parts of the repeat unit as unified pieces whose torsion angles were selected together rather than sequentially. Similarly, the size of the problem and the presence of significant partial charges on some of the atoms required more stages in the energy minimization. First the nonbonded radii (used with the softer nonbonded interactions) and partial charges were slowly increased over 14 to 20 steps. Then the full nonbonded and rotational potentials were used and the radii and charges were gradually increased to their normal sizes, requiring another 13 to 20 steps. Some variations in the stages were attempted, with the conclusion that the resulting structures were not affected by their minimization history; thus a total of 13 generated structures was considered as one ensemble for the extraction of properties. Fig. 4.11 shows an example of an energy-minimized structure.

4.4.4   Other Methods of Generating Amorphous Polymers

In this section we cite several more examples of the construction of an amorphous polymer model. In some cases, the chain propagation method is modified or followed by additional treatments; in the final two cases, it was not used at all.

In the first example, several refinements and additions to straightforward chain propagation were used by Fan and Hsu [66] to build a polysulfone whose repeat unit contains four phenylene units linked by ether, sulfone, and aliphatic groups. First, the van der Waals radii were reduced to 30% of normal during the chain-propagation phase; this was necessary to permit packing at the densities sought. Next, the relaxation process was conducted using both energy minimization and molecular dynamics, typically for 5 to 8 cycles. The full van der Waals radii and functional forms were used from the beginning, and the dynamics simulations of approximately 20 psec were conducted at temperatures from 300 to 500 K to allow the structures to escape from metastable high-energy minima. Other refinements included allowing the cubic cell to deform, and using an Ewald summation technique to account for the long-range tails of the nonbonded interactions. The unit cells of the 10 final structures remained very close to cubic, with a narrow distribution of cell parameters. Structural properties were calculated from the ensemble of 10 structures.

McKechnie, Brown, and Clarke [67] explored another method of chain generation for long (1000 monomers) polyethylene-like polymers. With the conventional propagation method, it was found to be impractical to generate densities higher than about 0.5 g/cm^3, but more importantly, there was an increasing discrimination against *trans* states as the growth proceeds. In the new method, self-avoidance effects are ignored except for those between sites separated by three others, i.e., so-called

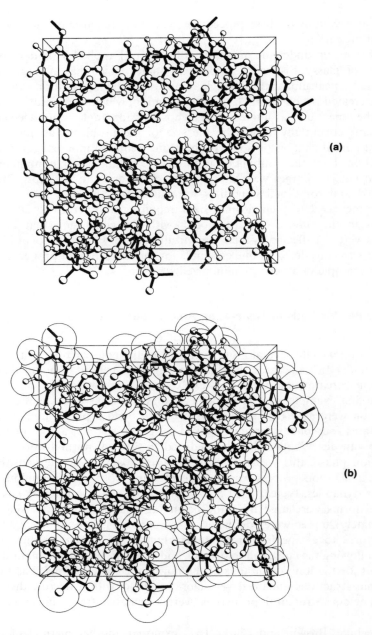

Figure 4.11. Energy-minimized polycarbonate structure. Atomic radii are reduced for clarity; in (b) the actual atomic radii are drawn as light lines. Reprinted with permission from Ref. 65. Copyright 1991 American Chemical Society.

"pentane interactions." While this promotes the correct distribution of conformational isomers, it leaves the starting model with serious overlaps, which must be carefully relaxed without altering the conformational distribution. Further, the authors wished to go directly to molecular dynamics without a minimization step, again to avoid changing the torsional distributions. Several attempts at gradual addition of the nonbonded forces failed or were awkward. The successful method found was to eliminate the hard core of the Lennard-Jones potential, replacing it with a constant for atom pairs separated by less than 85% of the sum of their van der Waals radii. Tracking the pair distribution function showed that the problem was resolved within the first few picoseconds of simulation; then it was possible to change over to normal dynamics with the full Lennard-Jones potential.

A more direct route to an amorphous model was taken by Smith *et al.* [68] in a simulation of atactic polyvinyl chloride. The ensemble consisted of 30 atactic chains of 12 repeat units each. They were aligned in extended conformations at a low density (no attempt was made at this point to introduce optimal packing of the chains, whose atactic nature made them irregular), and then subjected to molecular dynamics with periodic boundary conditions at 750 K. The heated, disordered system was annealed to 600 K and 450 K, at which the densities were 1.11 and 1.24 g/cm^3, respectively. The simulations were then continued for 1 nsec at each temperature.

As a final example, we cite the work of Winkler *et al.* [69] in which a quite different equilibration method not involving energy minimization or molecular dynamics was used. This work simulated melts of normal alkanes (tridecane $C_{13}H_{28}$, or octadodecane $C_{28}H_{58}$). After the chain-propagation method filled a unit cell with the required number of chains to obtain correct densities, the chains were subjected to a Monte Carlo reptation process. Reptation, or snake-like motion, involves removing a bond at one end of a chain and repositioning it at the other end; it is as if the chain had slithered along its length like a snake. One of the chains was chosen at random, and a reptation movement applied; the usual Monte Carlo step method was used to decide whether to keep the new configuration. The process continued with another random choice of chain and new bond placement. In this work, 192 million such Monte Carlo attempts were made to equilibrate the system. Additional studies with Langevin dynamics and the ordinary RIS method were compared.

4.5   Altering and Adding to the Material Model

The purpose of this chapter was to introduce methods for generating crystalline and amorphous domains composed entirely of polymer chains. In this section we consider other molecules that may be present, such as solvent, unpolymerized or partially polymerized monomer, and additives. These foreign molecules may be irrelevant to studies of bulk material properties, while in other cases, such as gas permeability, they are the point of interest in the system.

The phenomenon of the swelling of a polymer due to solvent is well known; even a highly networked, crosslinked polymer will swell in an appropriate solvent. This is not difficult to rationalize in conventional physical chemical terms. As the solvent penetrates within the interstices of the polymer network, it should push the polymer chains apart. At higher temperatures, the effect should be more pronounced as thermal energy increases the motion of all parts of the system. Similarly, the addition of plasticizers that increase the flexibility of a material can be interpreted by the same rationale. In what follows, we refer to the added molecules simply as "solvents," realizing that they actually can be molecules of conventional organic liquids, deliberately added plasticizers, unavoidable inclusions of unpolymerized monomer, or simply gas molecules from the surrounding air.

A direct approach to modeling solvent swelling can easily be envisioned. A material sample, constructed as described in this chapter, is inspected to locate any open volumes, or voids, between the polymer chains. Solvent molecules are inserted wherever possible, and periodic boundary conditions are used to generate the required image molecules. The problem occurs in finding spaces large enough to accept solvent molecules. There are several approaches suggested by the methods we have surveyed in this Chapter. The first is to build the sample under such conditions that it does not coil tightly, i.e., so that it has a lower density than normal. A second is to run molecular dynamics on the sample at elevated temperatures, using boundary conditions that permit expansion of the material, to produce a less dense model. A third possibility is to insert the solvent molecules into whatever small interstices can be found, realizing that this will create unfavorably short nonbonded contacts between solvent atoms and polymer atoms. These initial strains can be relaxed by energy minimizations that will cause the model to expand to accommodate the added solvent molecules; this is analogous to removing strains in the pure polymer itself.

An alternative approach would be to create a semi-infinite polymeric sample next to a semi-infinite extent of pure solvent, and to run molecular dynamics to allow the solvent to penetrate into the material. This approach for simulating the hydration of a polymer placed in solvent is physically realistic, but any model at an atomic level of detail would probably be much too large to offer any hope of seeing the effects of interest, because the diffusion of small molecules through polymers occurs slowly on the atomic and molecular time scale. Further discussion of the phenomena associated with such penetrant molecules is taken up in Chapter 7, which is concerned with diffusion, surface phenomena, and energy transfer in polymers.

4.6   Summary

The purpose of the operations described in this section has been to generate a model of bulk material, semi-infinite in extent, and with varying amounts of local order as needed to simulate real systems. The model produced should meet a number of structural criteria. While we will discuss aspects of polymer structure in more detail in the next chapter, we can state as a summary here that desirable characteristics of models include correct local chain geometry (bond lengths, bond angles), appropriate distributions of main-chain torsion angles, and realistic density. Statistical checks to evaluate the validity of a model and relevant experimental data will be discussed in the next chapter. Also there we will consider the dynamical aspects of equilibrium structure, such as local mobility and small oscillations about equilibrium.

5
Modeling of Polymer Structures

5.1   Introduction: Polymer Structure and Simulation Techniques

A point we stressed in the previous chapter was that polymer structure cannot be characterized as simply as, say, protein structure, in which one copy of the protein molecule can be treated as representative of every other copy in a crystal or in solution. This notion of average structure is valid for systems like proteins, even though individual molecules undergo thermal motion and fluctuate about the average so that at any instant, no single molecule actually exists in exactly the average structure. For polymers, where no single chain represents the average structure, the situation is more complicated, as is reflected in the diversity of approaches and computational effort expended in building realistic models.

Still, if one accepts the premise that polymer properties are governed by the details of molecular architecture, then the necessary starting point is a study of the microstructure of polymeric materials. Clearly this requires descriptions in terms of distributions and averages since no single representative structure can be assigned. These distributions may be obtained from an ensemble of independently generated single chains, or from measurements made on a single instance of a realistic multiple-chain material model. Examples of characteristics that can be evaluated include aspects of molecular geometry, such as measures of chain folding (e.g., end-to-end distance, persistence length, etc.); distributions of valence angles, torsional angles, and nonbonded distances; and broader characterizations of material structure, such as density, radial distribution functions, and spatial and angular correlations.

Structure can also be characterized as a static or a dynamic phenomenon. The structure of a polymeric material shows different aspects according to the time scale of the observations. Diffraction experiments, which see a time-averaged structure, present what might be considered the static picture of the partial order of the material, as evidenced by a diffraction pattern with some highlights and discernible features. Nuclear magnetic resonance, on the other hand, provides evidence of the dynamic nature of the structure, with periodic motions representing proton exchanges or conformational transitions of chemical groups. Other experimental methods, especially spectroscopy in other ranges of the electromagnetic spectrum, probe intermediate time scales. For example, the period of a fast vibration such as a C—H stretch that would be seen at one end of the infrared range, is about 10 femtoseconds (fs); this is what constrains accurate molecular dynamics to time steps of about 1 fs. The slowest motions in the IR range have a period of 1 picosecond or less, and are well within the simulation capability of a molecular dynamics run. Mechanical and viscoelastic properties depend on relaxation motions in the material; these phenomena may take microseconds, seconds, or much longer, depending on the material, the temperature, and other conditions. Direct simulation of phenomena at such long time scales is limited by computer resources.

As a result, one can envision the use of both static and dynamic simulation methods to study polymer structure. With either approach, the first part of the simulation is the construction of a realistic, atomic-level model, which was the subject of the previous chapter. Energy minimization of the constructed model produces a static structure in which dynamical aspects have been effectively frozen out; the structure has no kinetic energy, and the potential energy corresponds to close to 0 K. The study of the total energy, its components, and the balance of forces at the minimum-energy conformation is really a study of the enthalpy of the system, with no consideration of entropic factors. One approach to introducing entropy is to build and re-build the initial model, each time performing a complete energy minimization on each new model, and thereby creating a statistical ensemble of structures. Another approach is to use molecular dynamics to study the realistic, physical time evolution of the system while also generating an ensemble of structures. The obvious limitation in both methods is the amount of computer time required to generate many models or simulate even a few picoseconds of real time. While there is much evidence to suggest that molecular dynamics gives a very accurate and realistic picture of atomic and molecular motions, it is limited to comparison with data derived from experimental methods, such as NMR, that probe the very short-time behavior of the system. Simplified models based on larger elements (e.g., beads representing one or more monomers) have been evaluated for longer times.

The modern practitioner of molecular modeling must pay homage to the work of Flory, who set down an enormous body of principles and conclusions based on study only of local geometries and statistical extrapolation to systems [10]. While Flory had to describe phenomena in a closed form suitable for algebraic and relatively simple numerical evaluation, today's practitioner using computers can easily build and re-build models subject to varying assumptions, and evaluate their consequences numerically. Rather than devising a solution in closed form that is subject to simplifying approximations, one can actually generate ensembles of realistic structures and observe the behavior of statistical measures which are calculated and updated as each new structure is built.

We will begin the descriptions and case studies of polymer structure at the level of the single chain, and then proceed to the properties characteristic of bulk materials. We will then consider the comparison of calculated results of both a static and dynamic nature with the appropriate experimental methods. In this account, a number of case studies from the literature, embodying several different computational approaches, will be used. This should give the reader an appreciation of what can be done in this field. As always, we raise the caution that computational modeling methodology is undergoing continual revision and rapid development, and the current literature can be expected to yield much new work in the coming years.

5.2   Single Polymer Chains

In modeling the configuration-dependent properties of a single chain we make extensive use of the model-building methods explained in the previous chapter. The classical studies of polymer chain configuration depended on the assumption that short-range interactions are the most important in determining the coiling of the chain. This is the basis of the Rotational Isomeric State (RIS) method introduced at the end of Sec. 4.2.3. Rotational isomers, local minima produced by internal rotation about a main-chain bond, are considered as discrete states, and the relative energies of these states determine the probability that a given conformation will be found. Under the additional assumption of fixed bond lengths and bond angles, the set of rotational states along the bonds of a chain completely determines the chain's geometry. Expressing the population of rotational states at each site in this way leads to a statistical description of chain geometries that is based on very few parameters and which makes it relatively straightforward to evaluate configuration-dependent quantities.

The computer-based molecular modeling approach complements the theoretical RIS framework with computational experiments, while also permitting a greater degree of physical reality. In computer-based model building, as we have seen in Chapter 4, several assumptions can be relaxed:

- torsion angles need not be restricted to a discrete set of rotational states, but can be chosen continuously, with weighting based on the energy of the conformation as calculated from molecular mechanics.
- bond lengths and bond angles may be allowed to vary, again in a statistical way or by explicit energy minimization.
- the correct self-avoidance behavior of chains is taken into account.

The consequences for evaluation of chain properties such as persistence length or radius of gyration are obvious: rather than deducing the behavior from models using analytical theories, one can perform many model-building trials, with the desired set of conditions, and directly calculate the quantities of interest from the resulting ensemble. The variability and convergence properties can also be observed as the trials progress. These advantages of computer simulation are true for both single chains and multi-chain material models. If energy minimization or molecular dynamics is used, the details of internal geometric flexibility will be reflected in the final distributions of bond lengths, bond angles, and nonbonded distances; and the distribution of torsional states observed serves as an independent check on the validity of the RIS approximation.

With computer-represented structures, a number of the relevant quantities that characterize single chains are very easy to calculate at any stage of simulation, whether for single-chain or multi-chain models. Some of these include:

- end-to-end distance: this is simply the Cartesian distance between the two terminal atoms. Any number of other distances can be tracked, such as distances between functional groups or other chain markers. The distance vector has the components

$$\mathbb{R} = (x_N - x_1, y_N - y_1, z_N - z_1)$$

and the magnitude

$$R = |\mathbb{R}| = [(x_N - x_1)^2 + (y_N - y_1)^2 + (z_N - z_1)^2)]^{1/2}$$

- radius of gyration: this is a measure of the concentration or dispersion of mass in a rigid body and is another straightforward calculation based on the Cartesian coordinates of the atoms, which are maintained within the simulation software.
- characteristic ratio: $C = R^2/nl^2$, where R is the end-to-end distance, n is the number of units in the chain, and l is the effective length of each unit. For a fully extended chain, $R = nl$ so that $C = n$.
- persistence length: a measure of the mean distance traveled by the chain in the direction of the *first* bond or another vector expressing the initial propagation direction of the chain. If that vector is designated v, then $p = \mathbb{R} \cdot \mathsf{v}/|v|^2$.
- internal coordinate distributions: the distributions of rotational isomeric states, of individual torsions, of valence angles, or of any other internal coordinate of interest.

A short description of the value of single-chain modeling is given in the review paper by Clarke [61]; see Sec. 4.4.1. Chains were grown using a random-walk procedure weighted by torsional energies and always starting in the same direction; thus the distance in the direction of the first bond reached by a chain is proportional to the persistence length. This value differed with temperature because of the torsional weighting factor. The work gave a clear indication of how chains stiffen at low temperatures. It also was capable of showing the dependence of persistence length on the chain composition as the ratio of copolymers was varied.

The conformational energy used in chain propagation methods may be computed by any method, although here we have emphasized the use of empirical energy functions. An example of the use of a quantum-mechanical calculation to obtain torsional energy profiles is given in the paper by Darsey [70]. Rigid maps (see Sec. 3.2.3) for the central torsions about Si—O bonds in dimethylsiloxane were calculated with the *ab initio* technique, and these energy profiles were incorporated into a Monte Carlo chain growing program, in which 10,000 chains were grown, ranging in length from 22 to 250 bonds, and used to calculate the average end-to-end distance, the characteristic ratio, and their temperature coefficients. In this work, the point of the quantum-mechanical calculations was to derive the torsional potentials, not to geometry-optimize the monomers in different local minima (which was the goal of Ref. [57]). In particular, the chain-building exercises were carried out using a single standard monomer geometry. As noted at the end of Sec. 4.1, it would also be possible to use different monomer template geometries, where each template is chosen based on the torsional angles selected.

The molecular dynamics technique was used by Cho, Neuburger, and Mattice [71], who simulated a single polyisobutylene chain $C_{101}H_{204}$ at 400 K for up to 1.8 nanoseconds. The chain was started in an all-*trans* or nearly all-*trans* conformation with an end-to-end distance of 48 Å. While such an extended chain is clearly an idealization, it is simple to build; it is expected to coil rapidly during molecular dynamics, as the weakly attractive long-range portions of many nonbonded interactions exert their influence. Randomly initialized atomic velocities lead to torsional transitions, which also promote chain folding. The coiled chain had a characteristic length of approximately 6, while the experimental values are 6.3 to 6.9 at temperatures of 300 and 400 K. The authors believe that the lower simulated value results from the relative shortness of the simulated chain; a shorter chain encounters fewer self-avoidance conflicts because the likelihood of a chain's folding back on itself increases with chain length.

In this case study the authors also showed how the initially uniform monomer template geometry changed, with the bond lengths, bond angles, and torsion angles broadening to distributions. The two main-chain C-C-C angles, built initially at 127° for the unsubstituted methylene and 109° for the di-substituted one (see Fig. 5.1), broadened into smooth Gaussian-like distributions centered about 127° and 109°, respectively. The torsions, which were initially all *trans* (180°), evolved to clusters about the *trans* and the two *gauche* local minima (Fig. 5.2). The distribution of torsions about 180° was actually bimodal, with fewer occurrences of exactly *trans* geometry. The exact value of each bond angle and torsional angle for one specific monomer obviously depends on the details of the monomer's environment, including the long-range interactions acting on it.

Single chains or short oligomers are also convenient for calculations of vibrational spectra; in Sec. 5.3 below several case studies are given showing how conformation-dependent infrared bands were identified from calculations on oligomers.

Naturally there are many other simulations of single chains that can yield useful information, but these few examples serve to illustrate the point. Next we shall consider more complicated studies that begin with a detailed atomic material model built up from multiple polymer chains.

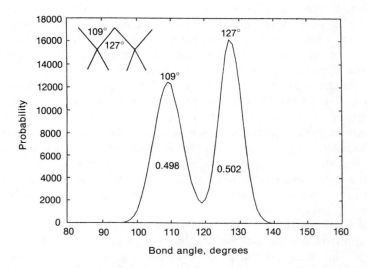

Figure 5.1. Distribution of main-chain bond angles in a polyisobutylene chain during molecular dynamics. In the initial model, the two bond angles are exactly 109° and 127° as shown in the stick figure at upper left. Reprinted with permission from Ref. 71. Copyright 1992 American Chemical Society.

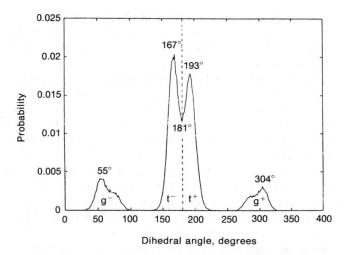

Figure 5.2. Distribution of dihedral angles resulting from polyisobutylene molecular dynamics. Note the bimodal distribution about the idealized *trans* value of 180°. In the starting model all torsional angles were exactly 180°; the figure shows that a small number of these have undergone transitions to *gauche* states. Reprinted with permission from Ref. 71. Copyright 1992 American Chemical Society.

5.3   Structural Characterization of Bulk Material

In this section we begin the discussion of simulations of multi-chain material samples, and the various methods of characterizing their range of conformational states and other structural properties. A first question in defining polymer structure is whether the material sample is even uniform, or whether it exists in different domains. In general a polymeric material at a temperature below its melting point is not uniform, but has separated into domains, some of which are quasi-crystalline in that there is considerable order, and others of which may be considered amorphous. In this section we shall discuss the characterization of materials that can be regarded as uniformly amorphous; some notes on crystalline domains are included in the next section, and thermal transitions between crystalline and amorphous states are considered in the last part of this chapter.

Certainly one useful basic descriptor of polymer structure is *density*, or mass per unit volume, which can be directly calculated from the locations and masses of all particles in the simulated system as it emerges from model building software or after it has been treated with energy minimization or molecular dynamics. The microscopic analogue of density, which is more useful for probing the microstructure at an atomistic level, is the *radial distribution function*. This expresses the probability of finding an atom within a spherical shell, with inner radius r and outer radius $r + \Delta r$, centered on another atom of interest. The radial distribution function may be defined to express the probability of finding an atom of the same type as the central atom of interest, some other specific atom type, or it can refer to any atom whatsoever. The ensemble-averaged radial distribution function is calculated by averaging the distributions for each central atom of the type of interest.

In calculating radial distribution functions it is customary to ignore atoms which are connected to the central atom by one, two, or three bonds (i.e., atoms involved with the central atom in bonds, valence angles, or torsion angles). These atoms have distances which are fixed or nearly fixed by the molecular connectivity. Thus the radial distribution is generated by the packing of nonbonded atoms (in the sense that they are four bonds or more separated) around the central atom. One expects the radial distribution function to have a moderately sharp peak at a distance equal to the sum of the two van der Waals radii; this is analogous to the first coordination shell about an atom in a liquid. Peaks corresponding to the second and higher coordination shell will be increasingly broader and less distinct. The sharpness and clarity of the peaks is a measure of the order in the system; in an amorphous system there should be no long-range order and there should be no more than two or three distinct peaks.

The density of a model depends greatly on how it was constructed as well as on the further simulation treatment. As discussed in Chapter 4, it is difficult to build an amorphous network or a single coiled chain at the densities of real materials, because chain propagation schemes begin to produce mostly failures that must be rejected on self-avoidance grounds. It is much easier, of course, to construct a perfectly crystalline domain at its maximum density. But for amorphous materials, it is likely to be necessary to build a model at somewhat too low a density, then use either energy minimization or molecular dynamics to obtain a more realistic density.

Energy minimization should always produce too high a density, assuming the process is started from a reasonably built model, and does not become trapped in high-energy local minima which retain large open spaces by some pathological circumstance of chain coiling. The case studies in Sec. 4.4.3 described some examples of the use of molecular dynamics to move a system out of such high-lying local minima; repeated cycles of minimization and dynamics serve to anneal a structure by allowing it escape from local minima and explore other minimization pathways. Energy minimization optimizes nonbonded contacts, taking advantage of the attractive part of the van der Waals potential and optimizing any oppositely charged electrostatic pairs. In energy minimization, there is no thermal energy to cause vibrations that would push atoms apart and result in a lower density. Thus the energy-minimized sample is a completely frozen material at its highest density.

Molecular dynamics offers other possibilities. First, the density may fluctuate over time and space as kinetic energy is transferred among different parts of the model. Secondly, the density is lowered by the presence of the kinetic energy, in contrast to energy minimization where there is none. Finally, it is possible for a material to undergo small internal conformational changes during dynamics; these may reduce strains, permit groups to explore new interactions, and otherwise explore alternative conformational states.

The difficulty of building realistic amorphous material models has been discussed already. In the first example of Sec. 4.4.3, Theodorou and Suter [64] built up fifteen samples of a vinyl polymer in its glassy state by a random-walk process, with torsion angles weighted according to their Boltzmann factor, and with consideration of self-avoidance. A several-step energy minimization procedure was needed to gradually relax the strains remaining from the construction process. The amorphous nature of the final model was confirmed by radial distribution functions for all of the types of pairs in the system. The total distribution functions, counting both intra- and interchain distances, but ignoring any distances which are fixed by the molecular connectivity, showed a few short-range peaks, but smoothed out rapidly beyond about 5 Å. In each case, the first peak occurred at the sum of van der Waals radii, representing optimized nonbonded contacts. A few more such coordination shells can be seen, then the material is essentially uniform. A geometric analysis of the individual chains in terms of their radii of gyration showed that they resembled unperturbed chains. A bond direction correlation function, based on the angles made by bond vectors throughout the chains, shows short-range correlation (which is necessary on connectivity grounds), but essentially random orientation for bonds more than a few centers apart. This indicated that the chains wandered randomly, with no memory of their initial direction beyond the first few bonds.

Another of the case studies of Sec. 4.4.3 was the extensive computational process undertaken by Fan and Hsu [66] to generate an amorphous polysulfone. As a measure of the removal of residual strains, they calculated an internal stress tensor, which is related to the force components remaining on each Cartesian coordinate of each atom, and found it to be suitably small. Measures of structure included the characteristic ratio, the radial distribution function, energy component distributions, the Hildebrand solubility parameter, the cohesive energy distribution, and the distributions of pairs of main-chain torsional angles. The torsion angle values were plotted on energy contour maps calculated for the monomers, and showed that virtually all the monomers were in low-energy conformations which fall within the energetically favorable contours (see Fig. 5.3).

Similar structural characterizations of a material model were presented by Hutnik *et al.* in their study of a glassy polycarbonate (see Sec. 4.4.3) [65]. Chains with degrees of polymerization of 35 and 151 gave good coiling behavior as shown by mean-squared end-to-end distances. Again the torsion values were plotted on monomer conformational energy maps and fell well within the low-energy regions (Fig. 5.4). Torsional distributions were also plotted in bar-graph form, and showed a broad, smooth distribution, in contrast to the two discrete RIS states. Pair distribution functions and bond directional correlation vectors completed the characterization of the material.

As a final example we cite the work of Smith *et al.* [68] who modeled atactic poly(vinyl chloride) by building a low-density periodic system and then introducing disorder with high-temperature molecular dynamics. After the chains were annealed to the two temperatures of interest, their characteristic ratios were calculated to be 7.6 ± 0.6 at 600 K and 7.3 ± 0.5 at 450 K. These compare with the values 7.4 and 6.4 calculated from RIS theory. The higher model values are probably due to the shortness of the chains (only 12 repeat units), which reduces the likelihood of their folding back on themselves, but they could also be a residue of the initial building process in which the chains were extended. The fraction of torsions within 60° of

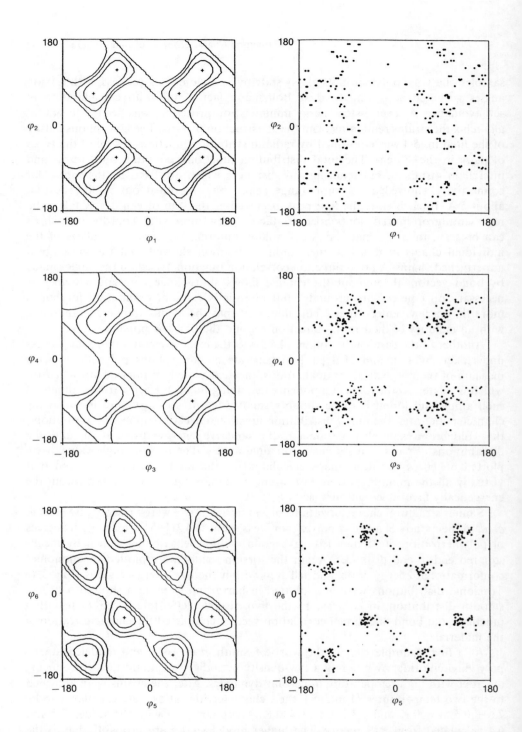

Figure 5.3. Calculated potential energy contours in sulfone-containing model compounds (left) and actual occurrences of torsion angles in carefully constructed polysulfone model (right). Reprinted with permission from Ref. 66. Copyright 1991 American Chemical Society.

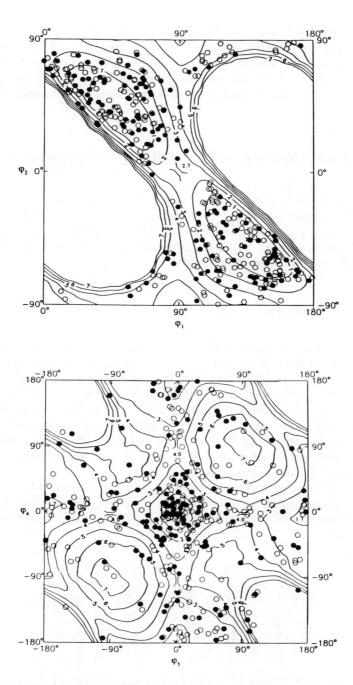

Figure 5.4. Calculated potential energy surfaces (contours) for model compounds and actual occurrences of torsion angles in energy minimized polycarbonate model (filled and open circles). Reprinted with permission from Ref. 65. Copyright 1991 American Chemical Society.

trans was 0.702 at 600 K and 0.673 at 450 K, compared to the RIS values of 0.704 and 0.656. The simulated material was further characterized in terms of radial distribution functions and correlations between the directions of groups of four atoms. The latter measure, which indicates the extent to which chains are aligned as a function of the separation between them, shows significant parallelism of the chains.

5.4   Domain Structure and Crystallinity in Polymeric Materials

One of the complexities of polymers is that the structure may vary considerably throughout a sample of material. Structural features that exist at levels somewhat larger than the single-chain level are the subject of polymer morphology. We have already referred to the idea of domains; thus we might speak of a crystalline domain within an otherwise amorphous material.

5.4.1   Crystal Modeling

When a polymer is cooled from the melt, its final density is intermediate between the density of the amorphous state and the ideal density of a perfect crystal. The earliest model used to explain this phenomenon was the *fringed micelle* model, in which *crystallites* were surrounded by amorphous regions; see Fig. 5.5. It was assumed that any single polymer chain threaded its way from one crystallite to the next, passing through many crystallites. Later experiments supported a different conclusion, namely that single crystals could be formed by folding a single polymer chain back and forth many times (Fig. 5.6); this arrangement is the so-called re-entrant chain folding configuration.

Elements of polymer morphology can be observed directly in light microscopes, electron microscopes, and newer forms of microscopy such as atomic force microscopy (AFM) and scanning tunneling microscopy (STM). Features such as spherulites,

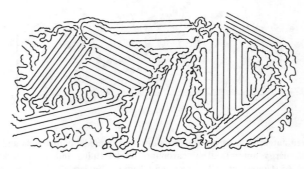

Figure 5.5. The fringed micelle model.

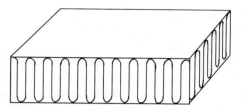

Figure 5.6. The more recent model based on a re-entrant polymer chain.

and sheaves or bundles of crystalline fibers are visible. They indicate that the nature of crystallinity in polymers is highly disordered, with many small crystalline domains growing adjacently but not maintaining a consistent orientation of crystalline axes [72].

As indicated earlier, it is a relatively simple model-building exercise to pack a set of identical linear single chains into a bundle. The packing possibilities become more complex when the individual chains are in helical form. Two papers by Napolitano [73] consider this problem for the packing of crystalline isotactic and syndiotactic *cis*-1,4-poly(1,3-pentadiene). Energy-function calculations on a trimer constrained to helical symmetry showed that its local minima fell near 2/1 and 3/1 helices, but only the 2/1 helix could generate an axis repeat of 8.15 Å and still fall near a local minimum. Chains in the 2/1 configuration were packed in a variety of space groups and then energy minimized, allowing the unit cell parameters to vary. The one with the lowest energy was then considered further; as a means of simulating the expansion of the crystal due to thermal energy without resorting to molecular dynamics, all van der Waals radii were increased by up to 0.3 Å and the structure was re-minimized.

5.4.2   Diffraction Data in Structural Modeling

Among the chief experimental methods for determining polymer structure is X-ray diffraction. Obviously this method is not sensitive to short-time fluctuations, and sees instead the long-time average structure, which is what we have been considering thus far in this Chapter. Typical of the process of using X-ray data to determine structure are four papers which will be briefly reviewed here. In the first, by Cageo *et al.* [74], the diffraction pattern consisted of a series of nonperiodic layer lines, consistent with a structure of parallel chains with a random monomer sequence. A study of rigid monomer models with discrete rotational states gave a set of theoretical spacings, which would imply very sharp diffraction peaks. Building short chains but allowing a continuous distribution of torsion angles produced a set of models whose internal spacings varied over a range of values, and therefore whose calculated diffraction pattern would be smoothed with broadened peaks. Detailed energetic modeling was not attempted, but was left as a future goal.

In a short communication, Miller [75] showed the reasoning used to interpret X-ray data and arrive at a unit cell for *it*-poly(methylmethacrylate). No energy minimization was involved in this work; the exercise consisted simply of building various models and considering their consequences for the X-ray pattern.

De Rosa *et al.* [76] studied the polymorphism of syndiotactic poly(1-butene). X-ray diffraction patterns from powder and fiber samples showed that the polymer can crystallize in two forms with distinct inter-layer spacings. Both model-built chains and energy-minimized models were constructed to compare with the X-ray data. Computed diffraction patterns were identified with the observed ones, and then energetic analysis was used to determine the energetically most favorable configuration.

Hobson and Windle [77] employed molecular modeling and calculated diffraction patterns to propose a solution to a long-standing question regarding the partial crystallinity of commercial polyvinyl chloride, which has a mixture of syndiotactic and isotactic chains. Semiempirical quantum-mechanical calculations on oligomers with 16 backbone atoms showed that the energetic preference for the syndiotactic structure is a fully extended *trans*-planar conformation. The minimum-energy structure for the isotactic form is a 3/1 helix, and it is difficult to rationalize any significant crystallization with two such different chains present in roughly equal proportions. However, conformational searches showed that the isotactic form can also adopt another local minimum whose axial repeat length is almost identical to that of the syndiotactic form; further, this alternative structure emulates the shape of the syndiotactic form quite closely, and thus is capable of co-crystallizing with it. Construction of crystalline arrays with varying proportions of the two types of chains, combined with calculations of the diffraction pattern, showed how certain diffraction peaks change intensity as a function of crystallite tacticity. This resolved the problem of how PVC samples of mixed tacticity could show significant amounts of crystallinity.

5.5   Dynamic Picture of Polymer Equilibrium Structure

To this point we have concentrated on structural aspects that may be considered fixed, i.e., characteristic of the structural features of the system as averaged over times that are long compared to the periods of most molecular motions. Now we consider atomic and group motions in the microscopic model of polymer structure. Much of the computational groundwork for polymer dynamical simulations, and the analysis calculations to characterize the results, were first set forth in the context of the dynamics of proteins, starting with the first calculation of the molecular dynamics of a globular protein in 1977 [20]. For further background the reader is referred to the books by McCammon and Harvey [21], Allen and Tildesley [22], and Brooks, Pettitt, and Karplus [23].

5.5.1   Vibrational Motions

Perhaps the clearest evidence that structures are not fixed and static is the infrared spectral patterns obtained from all systems. These infrared absorptions and emissions are a consequence of small harmonic or quasi-harmonic motions that are constantly executed by groups within any molecular structure. Other spectral regions contribute additional information associated with motions of other periodicities; most notably, nuclear magnetic resonance is increasingly used to probe motions on a time scale somewhat longer than that of molecular vibrations. Dynamic simulations can give a good account of the small and large motions in polymers, subject to the limitations of computer time needed to simulate various motions. A number of examples from the literature will show the methods used and the progress achieved by such studies.

Infrared spectroscopy offers an analytical means of probing polymer structure because certain frequencies are conformation-sensitive. Empirical relationships between structures and spectra can be derived from studies on model compounds that have known conformations, or which can be synthesized to include conformational restraints such as rings or cross-links. Computational methods should be able to reproduce conformation-dependent vibrational shifts, but this requires very accurate force fields. In parameter development, where the force field parameters are adjusted to provide the best fit simultaneously to structural, vibrational, and possibly other data, it is not uncommon for the fit to involve RMS errors of 30 cm^{-1}, with individual bands having discrepancies as large as 100 cm^{-1}. Therefore, any structural study using frequency calculations as its basis must be done carefully to assure the required accuracy.

One such example is an analysis of the low-frequency spectrum (from 0 to 600 cm^{-1}) of molten isotactic polypropylene [78]. In this work united atoms were used; that is, hydrogens were not explicitly represented, but were made part of the carbon to which they are attached. There were thus three atom types present: one representing the methyl side group, another for the main-chain methylene $-CH_2-$, and a third for the main-chain branch point whose carbon has one hydrogen. A force field was developed specifically for this system and used to calculate the spectrum below 600 cm^{-1} for an oligomer with 19 carbons in the main chain and 9 methyl side groups. The oligomer was constructed in conformations randomly generated from 3-state and 5-state isomeric models; it was found that one band was more sensitive to conformational changes.

In another study, Reynolds and Hsu [79] considered the vibrations of syndiotactic polystyrene. Their work was motivated by the recent synthesis of a polystyrene with over 90% syndiotactic nature. Experimental work indicated that this material formed into helices upon casting from dilute solution, but easily changed to an all-*trans*, highly oriented form upon annealing or drawing. The vibrational analysis, carried out on a monomer in the *trans* conformation, produced frequencies and potential energy distributions (in terms of the internal coordinates) that can be identified with the experimental infrared and Raman lines; the maximum error is about 45 cm^{-1} for one band, while most of the bands are much closer. A number of frequencies disappear, and new ones appear, upon annealing. The vibrational analysis made it possible to identify these conformation sensitive spectral bands, and deduce details of the structural change that takes place.

5.5.2   Larger Segmental and Concerted Motions

The dynamic picture of polymer structure has been built up from a series of experiments and theoretical calculations. Much the same conceptual evolution took place in the discipline of protein crystallography. When the first protein X-ray crystal structures became available, it seemed a natural conclusion that the structures were highly static, with only small vibrational oscillations occurring about the average structure. Studies of internal motions in proteins, together with NMR evidence, suggested that a variety of motions of considerable amplitude could occur with very little change in energy of the system; that is, the activation energy or barrier to these motions was small. One of the first such motional studies was of aromatic ring flips using NMR [80] and empirical energy function studies [81]. Later, calculations of the molecular dynamics of a protein [20] suggested that larger fluctuations could occur throughout the structure. These ideas have been reconciled with the concept of a static X-ray structure by recognizing that the latter represents a time-averaged view of a molecule that undergoes vibrations and fluctuations about its average structure.

As an example of the same process of studying small motions in polymeric systems, we can consider the work of Hutnik et al. [82] on the modeling of ring rotation for a main-chain phenylene group in an amorphous glassy polycarbonate. The creation of the material model has been described in Chapter 4 and in this Chapter. The computations of the energy and detailed conformation of the system, as the ring was forced to rotate, were done using the adiabatic or flexible-geometry mapping technique described in Sec. 3.2.3. The ring was rotated by a small increment (Fig. 5.7), then held fixed by an added torsional constraint potential, while the system was energy minimized with respect to all other degrees of freedom to remove any strains and close nonbonded contacts caused by the rotation. Iteration of this process mapped out the energy barrier to ring rotation, Fig. 5.8, while also showing which interactions were important and how the surrounding structure accommodated the ring rotation. The average barrier height for the three phenylene rings in a repeat unit was found to be on the order of 10 kcal/mol. The computational process used here was exactly the same as that first used to estimate ring-flip barriers in proteins and to correlate these barriers with experimental NMR observations [81].

From experience with proteins, it is to be expected that a variety of fluctuations with very low activation energy takes place along polymer chains. These involve motions of groups ranging in size from a few atoms to a few monomers, with concerted torsional changes such that there is no substantial movement of the fixed ends, somewhat as a child's jump-rope can be twirled while the two ends are essentially stationary. Another description of these motions that is particularly appropriate to polyethylene or polymethylene chains is the term "crankshaft" motions, as depicted in Fig. 5.9. A good example of a simulation of such motions is

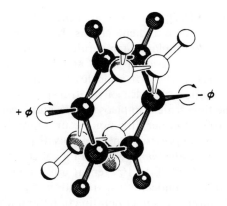

Figure 5.7. To produce a map of the potential energy for phenyl ring rotation in a glassy polycarbonate, the ring was rotated by small increments and constrained to the new position while all other degrees of freedom were subjected to energy minimization. Reprinted with permission from Ref. 82. Copyright 1991 American Chemical Society.

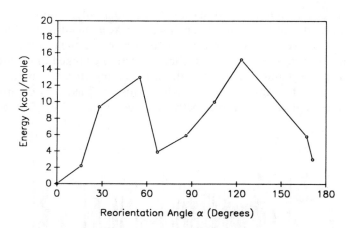

Figure 5.8. The potential for a phenyl ring flip, as mapped out by the process illustrated in Fig. 5.7. Reprinted with permission from Ref. 82. Copyright 1991 American Chemical Society.

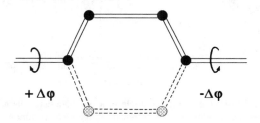

Figure 5.9. "Crankshaft" motion created by anti-correlation of torsions separated by three bonds.

given by Zhan and Mattice [83], who calculated the molecular dynamics of free and channel-confined 1,4-*trans*-polybutadiene chains. In a chain constructed in one of the crystalline forms, at a simulated temperature of 360 K, there were strongly correlated transitions among torsional states at CH—CH_2 bonds i and $i + 2$, of the form $A^{\pm}TA^{\mp} \leftrightarrow A^{\mp}TA^{\pm}$, where A indicates an anticlinal conformation and T indicates a *trans* conformation. An idea of the transition frequency and magnitude is given in Fig. 5.10. The time scale is in picoseconds, and it can be seen that torsional excursions as large as 100° in either direction occur approximately every 20 psec.

In a similar calculation on polyisoprene and polyethylene, Adolf and Ediger [84] considered what they termed the *cooperativity* of local conformational dynamics. In calculations on random coils of 70 to 100 repeat units, they looked for correlations between a torsion angle that underwent a transition (e.g., *trans* → *gauche*) and the torsion angles within 20 monomers in either direction along the chain. In about 30% of cases, when one torsion underwent a transition, the second-neighbor torsion responded within 3 psec. The other 70% of cases were so-called "isolated" transitions, and were accommodated by motions of only three or four adjacent backbone carbons; the more distant parts of the chain were essentially undisturbed by the torsional transition.

In a full molecular dynamics simulation of a model polymeric sample, Takeuchi and Roe [85] found that surrounding chains acted as a shield or coating around a central chain and prevented its overall reorientation. While the central chain rapidly tumbled about its local axes, the overall chain direction changed only slowly, and in response to the motion and relaxation of the surrounding structure matrix. This also serves as a rationale for simulation of single chains confined in a channel, and for the study of local chain fluctuations between fixed points. We will refer to other

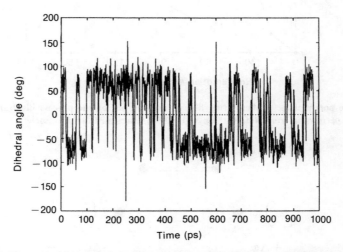

Figure 5.10. The dynamical history of a torsion angle in a polybutadiene chain. Note the frequency of transitions, the average torsional values at the extremes of the most common oscillations, and several excursions away from these averages. Reprinted with permission from Ref. 83. Copyright 1991 American Chemical Society.

aspects of these calculations in later Chapters. It should be mentioned that this model of a chain confined to a channel was first proposed and evaluated by Doi and Edwards [86]. Their goal was to explain the rheology of polymer melts in terms of the slow diffusion of the chains along the channels. This snake-like motion is known as reptation.

In a molecular dynamics simulation of a model polymer, Rigby and Roe [87] analyzed the temperature dependence of the distribution of free volume, or voids, within the network. Their analytical technique consisted of constructing polyhedra demarcating unoccupied volumes in the material. Above the glass transition temperature, there is a broad distribution of volumes — i.e., there are both large and small voids in the material — and this distribution narrows as the temperature decreases. The overall unoccupied volume increases with temperature, showing a definite inflection at the glass transition temperature, where the rate of increase becomes greater. Even below the transition temperature, there is considerable waxing and waning of cavities, in correspondence with the dynamic picture of polymer structure. This phenomenological picture of polymer structure will be important again in Chapter 7 when we consider diffusion phenomena.

5.6   Temperature Transition Behavior

As indicated at the end of the previous section, there are characteristic changes in polymer structure at critical temperature points. We will first characterize the physical picture of what happens at these temperatures, and then give some examples of simulations.

5.6.1   Phenomenology

As the temperature of a polymer sample is raised, its density decreases, and it loses any order which was present in the low-temperature state. The physical picture of the melted state is that there is considerable free volume, and the polymer chains are executing large-amplitude motions with no forces tending to restore them to any ordered state. These motions include transitions among the rotational isomeric states, diffusion-like wandering driven by Brownian motion, and the channel-confined reptation of the Doi–Edwards model. This accounts for the material's low tensile strength.

As the temperature is slowly decreased, the motions become smaller and less frequent. If there are no nucleation centers, or if the steric bulk of the chains renders crystalline ordering difficult, the material will not crystallize, but will cool through its normal melting point to become a supercooled liquid in a rubbery state (curve A-B-C in Fig. 5.11). At still lower temperatures (part D of the curve), motions become highly restricted, and the structure, though irregular, does not change. This is the

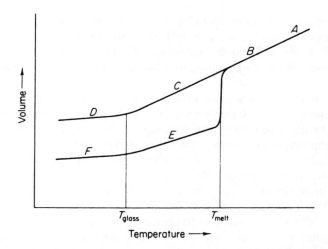

Figure 5.11. Volume-temperature curves for a crystalline polymer. (A) Liquid, (B) liquid with some elastic response, (C) rubbery region, (D) glassy region, (E) crystallites in a rubbery matrix, (F) crystallites in a glassy matrix.

glassy state, and the transition temperature or range at which it sets in is the glass transition temperature.

If crystallization does take place, crystalline domains will begin to form as the temperature is lowered through the melting temperature, and the volume will drop rapidly since the crystals are more dense than the amorphous material (curve A-B-E in Fig. 5.11). The physical state of the material is of small crystalline regions within a rubbery matrix. Below the glass transition temperature (segment F), remaining motions become small, and the material exists as crystallites within a glassy matrix. There is, of course, still thermal motion below the glass transition temperature, and it can be modeled by molecular dynamics simulations as discussed so far, but it is much restricted. As the above-described work of Adolf and Ediger [84] showed, conformational transitions are rapidly and locally compensated either by a corresponding transition of the opposite sense, or by smaller motions of a few adjacent backbone atoms.

5.6.2   Modeling Methodology

The above description of microscopic motions would appear to offer the possibility of determining theoretical glass transition and melting temperatures through molecular dynamics simulation. After building the model, removing initial strains or other modeling artifacts, and equilibrating the system with molecular dynamics at a low temperature, the temperature would be raised in small increments, giving the system enough simulation time to equilibrate at each new temperature, and observing the motions. Thermal transitions would be detected by changes in the motion, according to numerical criteria. The first problem to keep in mind in such a scenario is the definition of these motional criteria for melting and other transitions. The second is the limitation of computer time. The practical limit for equilibration at each temperature is on the order of 10 psec; if the temperature is raised by a 10°-increment every 10 psec, this corresponds to a rate of increase of 10^{12} degrees per second, which is hardly physically realistic. One has to be on guard against doing a simulation that has no physical significance; if the 10 psec equilibration period is not long enough for the material to respond to the change in conditions (which could be the case if a phase change occurs), the validity of the simulation is compromised. One way to evaluate a simulation involving a change in an external variable is to run it in both directions, i.e., in this case the simulation would be done with the material heated between equilibrations, then the direction would be reversed and the sample cooled between equilibrations. If there is hysteresis, then the methodology must be investigated.

5.6.3   Examples

The previously mentioned simulation by Rigby and Roe [87] showed that the free volume distribution can be used as a measure of thermal transitions. The overall cavity volume decreased as the simulation temperature was lowered, with an inflection at the glass transition temperature where the rate of decrease slowed greatly. The distribution of void volumes, however, seems to be less useful a measure; even though it narrows as the temperature decreases, there remain significant fluctuations even below the glass transition temperature.

A simulation by Sumpter, Noid, Wunderlich, and Cheng [88] concentrated on the competitive melting and crystallizing of a single crystal of polyethylene. The model system consisted of a bundle of all-*trans* polyethylene chains arranged in a perfect crystal; different models with varying amounts of chain-folding were studied (see Fig. 5.12). At temperatures near the melting temperature, the melting transition rate decreased as the amount of folding increased, but at temperatures 100 K higher than the melting point (the experimental melting point of polyethylene is 415 K), increased folding appeared to increase the melting rate. Naturally, it was necessary in this study to find methods to characterize melting and re-crystallization. The measure of the melt rate was the time it took for the radius of gyration to converge to a steady value, and the rate of crystallization was taken as the logarithm of the number of atoms oriented per unit time.

Further simulations by Sumpter, Noid, and Wunderlich [89] studied the nature of the internal dynamics of their model crystal and the mechanisms by which internal energy transfer occurs. Starting again from the perfect orthorhombic polyethylene crystal, with bundles of all-*trans* chains totalling to 6100 —CH_2— groups, they first looked for the onset of thermal disorder in simulations at 80, 430, and 488 K. A large number of conformational transitions cause a decrease in the end-to-end distances of chains. Although each specific "defect," or *trans*-to-*gauche* transition, has a very short lifetime, larger numbers of them occur as the temperature increases, producing

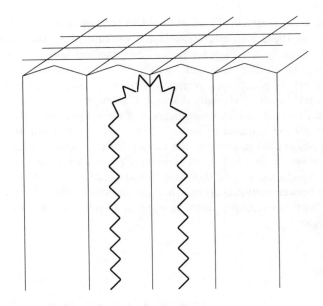

Figure 5.12. Chain fold in an idealized polyethylene crystal model.

thermal disorder. This is shown by histograms of the torsion angle as a function of time; the initially all-*trans* population clearly decreases and yields to increasing *gauche* populations; in fact, by about 8 psec in a 488 K simulation, the fraction and profile of the *gauche* population appears almost to have reached a steady state (Fig. 5.13). A "movie" sequence of snapshot graphics of the entire system, reproduced in Fig. 5.14 for a $T = 430$ K simulation, shows the changes in the initially ordered system as a function of time and temperature.

Studies on a larger system of up to 10,000 —CH_2— groups [63] showed the crystal readily breaking into domains even in low-temperature simulations. Visual inspection of views along the initial axis of the chains is sufficient to identify grain boundaries and concerted motions of domains. At higher temperatures, major disordering at the surface set in, and eventually bulk melting behavior was seen.

When an otherwise perfect polyethylene crystal was perturbed by placing a twist in one chain [90] (see Fig. 5.15), this defect moved rapidly to the end of the chain, where it was quenched. At higher temperatures, the defects were spontaneously introduced, as kinetic energy randomly concentrated in certain torsions and caused *trans*-to-*gauche* transitions. At a simulation temperature of 320 K and above, random torsional excursions of over 90° were frequent; this denotes general melting of the crystal. Further simulations [91] were aimed at understanding the nature of defect creation and transmission, and the activation energies and lifetimes associated with them.

Takeuchi and Roe [92] found that the glass transition temperature depended sensitively on model assumptions. They performed molecular dynamics simulations

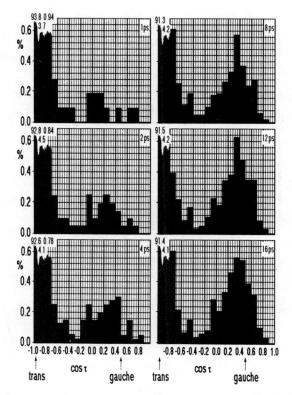

Figure 5.13. In the first 8 psec of molecular dynamics simulation of polyethylene, the torsion angles reached a steady distribution with a significant *gauche* population. Reprinted with permission from Ref. 62. Copyright 1990 American Institute of Physics.

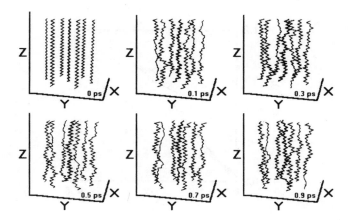

Figure 5.14. Even in the first picosecond of the molecular dynamics simulation at 430°K, there was a significant loss of order in the idealized crystal model. Reprinted with permission from Ref. 62. Copyright 1990 American Institute of Physics.

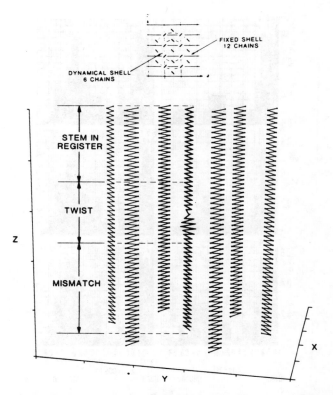

Figure 5.15. A twist defect introduced into the idealized polyethylene crystal model. Reprinted with permission from Ref. 90. Copyright 1991 American Chemical Society.

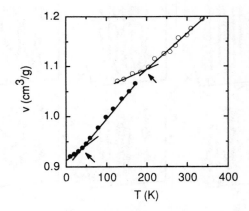

Figure 5.16. The glass transition temperature is detected as an inflection in the plot of specific free volume against temperature. —○—○—○—, PE model, —●—●—●—, FRC model (see text). Reprinted with permission from Ref. 92. Copyright 1991 American Institute of Physics.

on polyethylene-like chains of 600 —CH_2— groups with all the standard valence terms in the potential function (this was termed the PE model), and on a system of freely-rotating chains (the FRC model), i.e, one in which the torsional potentials were set to zero. In both cases, the glass transition temperature was obtained as the inflection point in the plot of temperature against volume (Fig. 5.16). In this figure, the volume at each point is obtained by a 120-psec dynamics simulation. Above the transition temperature, the greater disorder and frequency of large torsional excursions produced a more rapid increase in volume with temperature. The transition temperature for the full model was 201 K, while for the freely-jointed chains it was only 39 K.

5.7   Summary

In this chapter we have surveyed the theoretical study of polymer microstructures from both static and dynamic points of view. Some characteristics can be obtained by studies of single chains, while more realistic multi-chain models reveal additional information. Examples of building and simulating both types of models have been discussed.

Experimental techniques supply the information needed to guide modeling studies. Diffraction experiments provide a time-averaged view of polymer structure and indicate the degree and types of long-range order present. Spectral methods probe phenomena on time scales ranging from femtoseconds (for fast vibrations) to nanoseconds (for slower motions of segments or domains). Appropriate modeling techniques produce results which can be compared to this data.

The dynamic picture of polymer structure forms the connection with thermal behavior and offers the possibility of determining thermal transition points from dynamical simulations at a range of temperatures. The largest such simulations show spontaneous division of initially ordered structures into smaller domains. For the purposes of this chapter, the simulations provide a detailed picture of the dynamical equilibrium which characterizes polymer structure. They also contain a great deal more information about internal motions, processes, and energetics; the interpretation of such information sheds light on other properties of polymers, which are the subjects of the following Chapters.

6

Simulation of Mechanical Properties

6.1   Material Response to Mechanical Stress

Among the useful attributes of polymeric substances are the wide range of material properties obtainable as a function of three factors. The first is chemical composition, *i.e.* the type and sequence of monomers along each polymer chain, which is influenced by the chemical reactants, the polymerization conditions, and the catalysts used. The second is detailed multi-chain configuration, or three-dimensional arrangement of the polymer chains in the bulk material, which is influenced by the material processing conditions and the ambient temperature and environment. The third factor affecting properties is additives, which we will not consider here; some of the effects of additives, especially gas molecules and similar small penetrants, are of interest in the next Chapter. In this Chapter we concentrate on modeling and simulation methodology in its applications to explaining mechanical properties directly from the chemical composition and three-dimensional configuration of polymeric substances.

To approach or classify the great range of material properties so as to concentrate on specific phenomena, we first give some discussion of the range of phenomena under consideration and the categories of physical states of interest. In the domain of phenomenology, we can begin with small (infinitesimal) stresses and the response of the material at near-equilibrium conditions, then proceed to larger and more severe deformations; eventually the material reaches the condition of mechanical failure due to extreme conditions. Among physical states of materials, we can study amorphous *vs* crystalline behavior; the temperature dependence of the behavior, especially in relation to T_g and T_m, the glass transition and melting temperatures; and the degree of cross-linking in the material, which determines whether unlimited flow can occur.

The fundamental goal of material mechanical studies is to determine the relationship between an imposed stress σ and the responding strain or elongation ε. The factor which relates the two is the modulus. In the simplest case, the stress and strain are scalars assumed to be parallel to some reference direction, as in the case of a long, thin cylindrical sample of material being tested by tensile force along the long cylinder axis. In general, both quantities are tensors. The diagonal elements represent stress and strain along the Cartesian axes x, y, and z, while the off-diagonal elements represent shearing forces and responses through the xy, xz, and yz planes. The development of this formalism for macroscopic material samples is supplied by many texts on the strength of materials or materials science [93].

In simple terms, the behavior of polymeric materials can be summarized as follows. For an amorphous material well below T_g, the behavior is essentially that of a homogeneous incompressible solid undergoing elastic deformation. In the vicinity of T_g, both a flow response and a retarded elastic response are observed; a sufficiently cross-linked material will resist flow, as the cross-links extend throughout the material sample and form a non-disruptible network. Crystalline materials are of particular interest at temperatures from the vicinity of T_g up to T_m; they exhibit highly non-linear, directional responses. Above the melting temperature, crystallinity ceases to exist, and all polymers exhibit viscoelastic flow whose nature depends on the amount of cross-linking and the average molecular weight. Here the term flow does not refer to macroscopic phenomena such as laminar flow, but rather to a molecular response for which there is no restoring force, and which is therefore unbounded on the microscopic level.

At the molecular level, the goal of simulation is to investigate the mechanisms of deformation and response to stress through atomic-level motions. We wish to be able to make quantitative predictions, and to understand and differentiate the effects of chemical composition and molecular architecture. Most of all we wish to be able to identify or define phenomena that can be controlled by altering the material, so as to design the polymer's mechanical responses to be suitable for given tasks.

The qualitative physical picture of these types of behavior can be visualized in terms of thermal motions of polymer chains within the surrounding matrix. Far below T_g, the chains are tightly confined and can do little more than execute small-amplitude vibrations about their average positions. Near T_g, greater amplitude motions become possible, and spontaneous backbone conformational transitions offer possibilities for chain reorientation on a larger scale; chains can begin to slip past each other. As the temperature increases, the motions increase still more. In crystalline polymers, the crystalline domains are surrounded by a glassy matrix which begins to soften and allows the orientational aspects of the system to be lost. At the melting temperature, crystalline and amorphous polymers alike lose short-range order and chain mobility continues to increase. In the melt, chains will slip past each other unless prevented by a cross-link network; the rate of slippage will depend on the average length of the chains (and thus the molecular weight). Other factors include the shape of the chains, i.e., whether they have "knobby" sidegroups that can prevent easy relative motion; and the charges or polarity of sidegroups, which can also form weak attractions whose aggregate resists deformation.

Molecular simulation is naturally best suited to the domain of short times and small deformations, but both by itself and in combination with known macroscopic principles of material response, simulation can be useful in understanding phenomena that occur on longer time scales or involve larger responses. It should be understood how short the time domain involved actually is compared to real phenomena which we normally think of as "fast." For example, the response of a structural element of an automobile body during a crash test is studied in the millisecond time scale; but full-scale detailed molecular simulations at present are limited, for practical purposes, to a few nanoseconds. Thus crash simulations treat materials from a macroscopic point of view, making use of measured material properties and constitutive equations. Even if advances in computers and in simulation software techniques permit simulations that are three orders of magnitude longer (thus into the microsecond domain), it is not likely that such computations will replace macroscopic models. They can, however, give much information as to the molecular mechanisms of energy absorption and other phenomena of interest, and thus be useful in designing new materials.

6.2   Simulation Studies with Simple Oligomers

As in any attempt to simulate physical behavior, the key to success is an appropriate matching of available computational techniques to the characteristics of the system and the phenomena of interest. At the molecular level, the techniques of energy minimization, molecular dynamics, and analysis of the energy contributions can be applied to single chains and to bulk material models of varying degrees of sophistication. The most realistic approach is certainly to perform molecular dynamics at the full atomic level of detail, using a material model developed as described in Chapter 4. But information can be gained with simpler models of several types. Simpler models permit longer simulation times, and the results can be valuable if the consequences of the simplification are understood (*e.g.*, through comparative studies in which a variety of models have been tried on the same problem).

Some studies of mechanical properties have been performed using only single oligomer chains. Obviously these ignore the effects of material architecture, but they require much less computation. They also offer the advantages of a small model which can be treated accurately, in that it is possible to use all-atom representations and more detailed force fields. The microscopic model for the external stress is very simply expressed as forces pulling apart the two atoms at the ends of the chain, and the material response is observed as atomic displacements and internal coordinate changes all along the chain.

With empirical force fields, it is also possible, when considering a single chain in a specific conformation, to evaluate *analytically* the force required to produce an elongation. The restoring forces within the chain are the force constants for the various internal coordinates; the trigonometric and algebraic manipulations required to express these in terms of a chain stretch may be complicated, but the concept is straightforward. This is because any atomic displacement affects the bond lengths, bond angles, torsions, and nonbonded interactions in terms of which the force field is expressed. This approach was used by Enomoto *et al.* [94] to determine the elastic modulus and atomic displacements for planar zigzag vinyl polymers and helical isotactic polypropylene. The results were comparable to experimental values, though an exact comparison is hindered by the lack of "ideal" (perfectly crystalline or ordered) samples that correspond to the simulation conditions.

Two examples of direct calculations on single oligomer chains are described here; in both cases the external stress was a tensile force applied to the end-atoms of the chain. In the first study, Bleha, Gajdos, and Karasz [95] built *n*-hexadecane ($C_{16}H_{34}$)

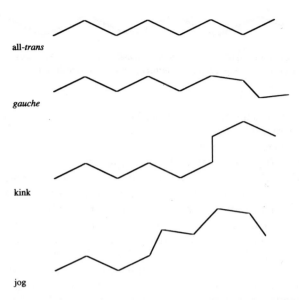

all-*trans*

gauche

kink

jog

Figure 6.1. All-*trans* chain and various types of defect introduced into it. A tensile force was then applied to the chain ends and the oligomer was energy minimized subject to the tensile force (see text and Ref. 95).

chains with various non-*trans* "defects" (see Fig. 6.1) and simply applied a tensile force to the chain ends to observe the yield mechanisms. The structure was first energy minimized in the conformation as built; then the tensile force was applied and the energy minimization process was continued. In graphs of the molecular mechanics potential energy versus percent elongation, there were clear yield points at 5 to 10% elongation associated with conformational transitions that enabled the chain to lengthen in response to the imposed force. By monitoring all the internal coordinates, as well as the energy contributions, the authors developed a picture of how the imposed stress was taken up in bond angle bending, and to a lesser extent, bond stretching and torsional deformations. A value for the tensile modulus was computed from the curves, assuming a cross-sectional area of $1.824 \, \text{Å}^2$ for a single chain. Comparative studies of this type could be used to compare the effects of chemical composition in different polymers.

Essentially the same idea was employed by van der Werff, van Duynen, and Pennings [96], who began from the observation that the tensile strength of polymeric fibers is about 1/5 of the theoretical breaking strength of carbon–carbon bonds. Their study of single polyalkane chains was aimed at finding out how chain folds permit elongation to occur at a fraction of the bond-breaking force. Eight different types of "defects" were generated. Each was first minimized with a restraining force (to maintain the defect), but no tensile force; then the energy was re-minimized after each of 20 incremental increases in the tensile force. The force-strain curves again showed clear yield points. A more detailed analysis of the energy components than in the previous example revealed that deviations of the bond angles from their

Figure 6.2. Response (exaggerated) of oligomer chain to tensile force: —— **All-*trans* conformation, energy minimized with no tensile force.** —— **Energy minimized subject to tensile force.**

strain-free values stored about 25% more potential energy than bond stretching. Individual chain tracings are shown for the chain as first built, and as energy minimized at the maximum tensile force; see Fig. 6.2.

These single-chain studies give detailed and precise information about the microscopic yield mechanisms of a chain under idealized circumstances. It is clear, however, that there are also interesting phenomena and contributions from the spatial arrangement of chains in an amorphous network. To study such a system directly requires a multi-chain material model, using the basic concept of the periodic box as described in Chapters 3 and 4. The analogy to the imposed tensile force on a single chain is a deformation of the periodic box. The techniques of energy minimization and molecular dynamics have both been applied; in the application examples of the next section, we recount examples of both techniques, applied to amorphous, crystalline, and melted polymers.

6.3   Amorphous Polymer Simulations

6.3.1   Discussion of Material Behavior

The wide range of mechanical properties of amorphous polymers can be simplified using two basic principles developed for analysis of macroscopic materials. The *superposition principle* states that stresses are additive, and that the effects of a complicated temporal and spatial stress pattern can be understood by analyzing it into components and evaluating the response for each component. Thus studies involving pure uniaxial tension or one component of shearing are valuable and can be added together to understand more complicated stresses. The *time-temperature equivalence principle* states that the viscoelastic response at one temperature can be understood and predicted from measurements made at another temperature, and that effects that take place over longer times are equivalent to what happens in a shorter time but at a higher temperature. The qualitative mechanistic rationale is that molecular motions assume higher amplitude as the temperature increases, and that the chance fluctuations required to permit the material to respond to a stress occur with greater probability as a result of the increased thermal motion.

Below the glass transition temperature T_g, amorphous materials exhibit pnenomena of elastic response and recoverable flow. Near T_g, the flow may become non-recoverable. In the elastic case, we want to compute the associated moduli; in case of flow, we want to be able to characterize its viscosity. In both cases, simulations also have as a goal the elucidation of detailed molecular mechanisms.

Another helpful empirical rule of thumb is the idea of *corresponding* states. The basis of this idea is that chemical composition determines the short-time (or low-temperature) behavior of an amorphous polymer. Processing, which affects the arrangement of chains, leads to deviations in the long-time behavior. Correspondingly, chemical composition is the major determinant of T_g; that is, all polystyrenes, regardless of branching, tacticity, and crosslinking, have a roughly similar T_g and similar behavior in short-time, low-temperature mechanical properties. (Exceptions to this statement are provided by polystyrenes of very low molecular weight, which have a lower T_g, and those with a high degree of cross-linking.) The principle of corresponding states is that materials will behave similarly at temperatures that are similar relative to their T_g.

At temperatures above T_g and on into the melted state, the viscous behavior is principally determined by molecular weight, if the polymer is not very cross-linked. For highly cross-linked polymers, the behavior of the network is determined by the degree of cross-linking. There is a critical degree of cross-linking, sometimes called the gel point, at which the cross-link network extends continuously throughout the sample, and which is the dividing line between viscoelastic fluids and viscoelastic solids. Below this critical degree, substances are referred to as "linear" or thermoplastic; above it, they are called "cross-linked" or thermoset. These terms adequately depict the differences in macroscopic behavior.

In summary then, a major goal of simulation is to give a reasonable account of the T_g, or at least to predict correctly the relative ordering and magnitude of differences for T_g of a series of structures. That information plus the principle of corresponding states gives a good idea of the general behavior of the glassy polymer. Higher temperature behavior, on the other hand, will be determined principally by either the molecular weight or the degree of cross-linking.

6.3.2 Application Examples

We have already seen some examples of the determination of T_g from molecular dynamics simulations (Chapter 5); with this background, we are now ready to review several examples of simulation evaluation of properties for glassy polymers below the glass transition temperature. The general approach is to compute the consequences of small deformations of the periodic box which encloses a realistic multi-chain material model; this can be done by energy minimization or molecular dynamics subject to the constraint of a periodic box of fixed size and shape. The interpretation of mechanisms is made difficult by the detail of the model; extensive analysis may be required to characterize the atomic and group shifts that took place during a simulation.

One of the first large-scale calculations of this type was designed and carried out by Theodorou and Suter in 1986 [97]. They stated their goal to be the development of methods for determination of elastic constants for amorphous glassy polymers by calculation of small-strain deformations of detailed model structures. The construction of the models, and their structural characterizations, were discussed in Chapters

4 and 5 (Refs. [64, 65, and 82]). They first observed that the tight confinement of individual chains in the glassy matrix made entropic contributions negligible; that is, any single chain could access only one conformational state, about which it executed "solid-like" vibrations. Accordingly, enthalpies, which are what are obtained from conformational energy calculations and energy minimization studies, could be considered to govern the state of the system. Highly converged energy minimization calculations were carried out for a carefully constructed model both in its original state, and after deformation. Three types of deformation were considered: *uniform compression* (or dilatation), which is a shrinkage (or expansion) of all three axes of the cubic unit cell; *pure shear*, which was taken to be perpendicular to the *z*-axis, along the *x*-axis; and *uniaxial tension* or tensile strain along the *x*-axis. All deformations were small; for example, the maximum volume change was less than 0.1%. The computed Young's modulus, bulk modulus, and other quantities were all within 15% of the best experimental estimates; most quantities were within 5%. The detailed model assumptions and computational procedures are carefully presented in the original paper.

Similar methodology was applied to another polymer, the glassy polycarbonate studied in Refs. [65] and [82]. In this study [98] the calculated moduli were all somewhat higher than experimental values; this was believed to be due to the relatively small size of the periodic cell (485 atoms) and the high rigidity of the polycarbonate repeat unit. The expansion of the unit cell was extended much further than in the previous work. At 6 to 7% shear strain, yield phenomena similar to those discussed above in the simulation of simple oligomer chains were observed; these were attributed to large phenylene ring rotations, carbonate group reorientations, and rearrangements of the isopropylidene unit. These phenomena clearly show the complicating effects of the more detailed internal structure of this polymer, as compared with the simple vinyl polymer model used in the previous work.

In a second example, Brown and Clarke [99] carried out a series of simulations designed to model directly the behavior of a polyethylene-like system over a wide range of temperature (10 to 500 K), and to yield quantitative information about both elasticity and viscoelastic flow. They built a model of a 1000-site chain using a modified self-avoiding walk, followed by molecular dynamics and energy minimization to produce a relaxed sample. They then located the T_g from a volume-temperature plot; the volumes were taken from molecular dynamics-equilibrated systems simulated at a series of temperatures (Fig. 6.3). A small range of experimental densities for molten polyethylene is shown as a comparison and calibration of the simulation results. The deviation is systematic and apparently constant; the quantitative agreement was quite good.

The equilibrated samples were then subjected to a simple tensile force, with resulting elongations of up to 100% during dynamical simulations of up to 1 nanosecond. It is important to note in this work that the *applied tension* is the independent variable; both the *effective* stress on the material and the responding strain are dependent variables (for an analysis of these concepts and their correct interpretation in microscopic simulations, see Ref. [100]). Examples of the results are shown in Fig. 6.4. As expected, the material deforms much more slowly at low temperatures; a given elongation is associated with a larger applied tension. Beyond about 20%

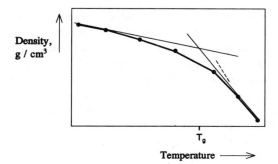

Figure 6.3. Determination of simulated T_g from variation of density with temperature. Each point represents a molecular dynamics simulation from which the density was calculated. Dashed line shows experimental data for molten polyethylene. (After Fig. 1 of Ref. 99).

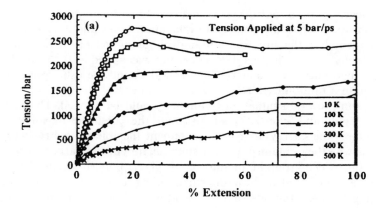

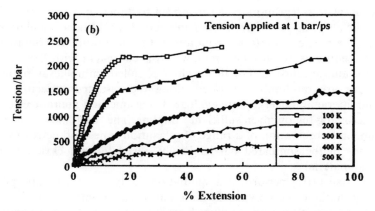

Figure 6.4. Measured tension as a function of percentage extension of a realistic material model. The data at each temperature represent the average of five independent molecular dynamics samples. Reprinted with permission from Ref. 99. Copyright 1991 American Chemical Society.

elongation, the material begins to yield, and the extension increases rapidly with small increases in the tension. The authors conclude that the results are a useful simulation of realistic behavior, despite the very short durations and high rates of deformation. The experimental phenomena appear to have been well simulated by the atomistic-level calculations, although not quantitatively. The calculated yield stress and strain are much larger than observed values, which is rationalized to arise from the slow response of the material to the very rapid deformation. In fact, comparing two sets of calculations, one with tension applied at 5 bar/psec and the other at 1 bar/psec, indicates a trend in the correct direction, namely, toward lower values when the applied load is less.

The third case study recounted here involves an examination of the processes by which amorphous materials relax residual strains even at temperatures well below the glass transition point [101]. Such processes should be important to the material properties, especially at longer times or slower rates of deformation, as in the phenomenon of creep. This study involved the relaxation behavior of a methyl acrylate sidegroup in a polyethylene matrix. Experimentally, nuclear magnetic resonance shows a broad distribution of relaxation times and associated activation energies. To simulate the situation, an amorphous model of material was built of n-$C_{24}H_{50}$ chains; one methyl acrylate sidegroup was added at the central carbon of one chain. A periodic box of material was bounded, and the usual precautions were taken to obtain a randomized, relaxed starting system.

At this point, several simulation techniques could be applied. The method used by Hutnik, Argon, and Suter [82] was to rotate the sidegroup by small increments and re-minimize the energy after each increment (flexible geometry mapping, Sec. 3.2.3). In this way they obtained a quasi-static picture of the barrier to rotation of a main-chain phenylene group in an amorphous glassy polycarbonate. The relaxation mechanisms are indicated by how the surrounding atoms move out of the way of the rotating group. Another alternative would be molecular dynamics, which would have to be simulated for long enough to observe barrier-crossing behavior. In the present case, this is unlikely since the NMR evidence indicates that relaxations of the methyl acrylate sidegroup are characterized by times on the order of 10^4 nanoseconds, while a simulation of even one nanosecond would be a calculation of some magnitude. The barrier to internal rotation of the sidegroup was obtained from a mapping procedure as about 6 kcal/mol, which is consistent with these frequencies. Therefore the authors chose a statistical technique called umbrella sampling, in which conformations are randomly generated along the assumed trajectory and their internal and interaction energies are evaluated. This method guarantees coverage of the barrier-crossing region given sufficient sampling. The results were consistent with the experimental observation of a range of relaxation times and activation energies; the variations in the simulated barrier height correlate with close-range packing effects in the material.

Fan and Hsu [102] performed a simulation study of an aromatic polysulfone, beginning by building the polymer in an assumed cubic unit cell and obtaining an average density from 10 energy minimized structures slightly below the actual density [66]. For each of the 10 samples, they imposed a uniaxial load and re-minimized the energy under constant stress. The deformation step size was 0.05%, applied in six increments in both the compressive and expansive directions (thus the unit cell was deformed over the range of -0.3% to $+0.3\%$). The authors note that there is evidence of irreversible deformation, even for small conformational changes. This is thought to be due to barrier-crossing motions, though structural details were not reported. Since the structure of this polymer is somewhat more complicated than that of those discussed so far, it is indeed likely that the potential energy surface contains many more small local minima between which the barrier crossing behavior can take place. These observations corroborate those of the previous paper that relaxation processes occur even well below the glass transition temperature.

An important simulation study, which demonstrates the dependence of mechanical properties on the conformational and configurational details of the material, was done by McKechnie et al. [103]. They built four independent polyethylene-like models, using their earlier methodology [99] but varying the details of the random chain growth acceptance criteria and the dynamical annealing process. The models differed in terms of percentage of *trans* bonds, density, and long-range order. The measured tensions and loads were plotted as functions of extension as the samples were subjected to uniaxial tension increasing at the rate of 5 bar/psec. The initial elastic response (up to 10% elongation) was quite similar for all four samples, then significant differences were observed. The model with the highest percentage of *trans* bonds (and thus the most oriented material) generated the largest stress, while the least resistance was offered by the highly coiled model. The other two models, which were intermediate in terms of orientation, showed different behavior which must be attributed to their contrasting preparation history and consequently different configurational properties.

The starting point for the discussion of amorphous glassy material behavior was the relatively low thermal mobility of the chains within the tightly packed glassy matrix. In such surroundings it is reasonable that relaxation motions, such as the rotation of a sidegroup, are restricted by the unfavorable nonbonded contacts that are created when the group moves from its starting location. But these contacts can be greatly reduced by very small displacements of the interacting atoms, which can make these small movements with little rise in the energy of the surrounding chains. Earlier NMR and molecular mechanics studies on the densely packed core of globular proteins showed the same phenomena [80, 81]. If the rotation barriers are low enough, the motion over the barrier is essentially random, diffusive behavior driven by fluctuations in the surrounding matrix. Thus the interior of a glassy polymer resembles a sluggish fluid in which thermal motions are highly damped.

6.4 Simulation of Crystalline Polymers

As stated above, a cold crystalline polymer consists of crystalline regions "frozen" within a matrix of glassy amorphous polymer; the material has the characteristics of a hard elastic solid. If the degree of crystallinity is high enough, the material can exhibit the behavior of soft metals, with significant anisotropy and non-linear effects.

Above the melting temperature, crystallinity is lost, and the viscoelastic behavior is similar to that of amorphous polymers above their melting temperatures, depending on the molecular weight and the degree of permanent cross-linking.

In the region of most interest, between T_g and T_m, the material is non-linear, and the effects of glide planes and dislocations can become evident. The behavior can change permanently after an initial *conditioning stress* which orients the crystalline regions and increases the degree of crystallinity along the axis of the stretch.

While polymeric materials are never completely crystalline, the ideal case can be considered as a limit to crystalline behavior. A method for calculating the characteristics of an ideally perfect polyethylene crystal was set forth in Ref. [104], where the methylene group parameters were taken from a force field parameterized for *n*-butane. The structure of the unit cell was optimized by energy minimization, allowing both the 6 unit-cell parameters and the atomic coordinates to adjust. The elastic constants were obtained from the analytical second derivatives at the minimum point, and were used to calculate the Young's modulus and the compressibility. The longitudinal deformation behavior was obtained from the longitudinal phonon states. For directions perpendicular to the orientation of the chains, properties were evaluated by making finite deformations and re-minimizing the energy; this was used to obtain the ultimate stress at which the material separates (tears). The Young's modulus calculated for deformations along the chain length was somewhat high compared to experimental values, but this was likely to be because the simulation used a perfect crystal, while even highly oriented laboratory samples do not achieve 100% crystallinity. The energetics of these deformations are determined principally by distortion of valence angles and to a smaller extent bonds. In the perpendicular direction, however, and in shearing deformations, the energetics are determined by the nonbonded forces between chains, making the material much less resistant; tearing occurs at 6–10% elongation perpendicular to the chain axis.

Application of similar methodology to poly(vinylidene fluoride), or PVDF [105], produced a force field that was found to have nine stable structures, four of which correspond to well-characterized crystal forms of PVDF. The derived force field was used to establish that each structure was mechanically stable (i.e., a true local minimum on the potential energy surface), and to calculate cell parameters, elastic constants, and other properties.

Yang and Hsu [106] computed properties of crystalline unit cells of three polymers using simulation methods similar to those used by Fan and Hsu [66] in their study of the properties of an amorphous polymer. They built crystalline domains for polyethylene, poly(*p*-phenylene terephthalamide) (PPTA), and poly (*p*-benzamide) (PBA) using small van der Waals radii to facilitate close packing, then raised the radii to the normal values during a process with alternating cycles of energy minimization and molecular dynamics. Available diffraction data guided the model-building for PE and PPTA. PBA has not been extensively characterized, and was modeled along the lines of the two better-known structures; from the computed crystalline structures, diffraction patterns were calculated for comparison. Elastic constants were evaluated by the now-familiar method of re-minimization subject to an axial stress or shear force on a plane. Again the elastic constants, especially those parallel to the orientation direction, were somewhat too high. The source of the mechanical properties was largely bonds and bond angles for resistance to axial stretch, and interchain hydrogen bonds (or nonbonded interactions for PE) for shear resistance. Fig. 6.5 illustrates the relative sizes of the energy contributions for PE and PPTA. Unlike PE, PPTA forms interchain hydrogen bonds and has significant group dipoles that contribute to the stabilization of the crystal. PPTA is therefore capable of storing approximately ten times as much energy in its internal coordinates. This case study is an especially interesting example of the relationship between detailed molecular structure, including polarity and its effects in producing nonbonded interactions, and material behavior.

In a related study, Reynolds and Hsu [79] used a normal vibrational analysis of syndiotactic polystyrene to compute a theoretical modulus from the longitudinal

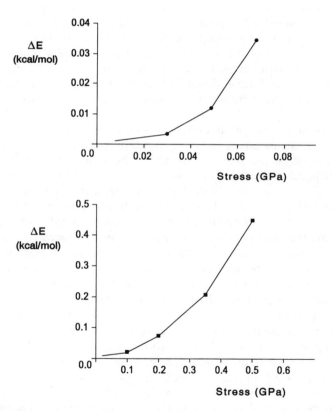

Figure 6.5. Nonbonded interactions supplied the largest contribution to the energy of shear deformation (see simulations of Ref. 106).
Above: Polyethylene has no polar groups, no hydrogen bonds, and very small residual atomic charges. The van der Waals contribution is shown, and all others (bond stretch, angle bend, torsion, and electrostatic) are well over an order of magnitude smaller.
Below: PPTA has numerous internal hydrogen bonds and charged groups. The hydrogen bond contribution is plotted; all other contributions are an order of magnitude smaller.
Note the different vertical and horizontal scales in the two figures.
(After Figs. 5 and 7 of Ref. 106).

acoustic mode. This is based on the analysis of a single chain, does not include any contributions from intermolecular forces, and is expected to represent a lower limit.

6.5   Melted Polymers

Above the melting temperature, order begins to disappear and all polymeric materials are characterized by the entanglement of chains, which must be undergoing larger internal motions, and spontaneously creating and annihilating larger voids or free volumes than at lower temperatures. One model of polymer response to deformation under these conditions is the picture of the chains slipping past one another by motions similar to a snake's propulsion; hence the term "reptation" for this model. The detailed simulation of these motions would demand very long calculations, as can be seen from estimates of the frequencies of the motions involved. NMR evidence also suggests that the chain motional phenomena occur on the nanosecond and longer timescale, so that simulations of many hundreds of nanoseconds would be required.

One way to shorten the simulations is to use a more mobile chain model, realizing that the behavior calculated may not be quantitatively correct, although by appropriate scaling it may be possible to rationalize the results. Gao and Weiner [107] performed such calculations of melt viscoelasticity; their model contained freely-jointed chains with harmonic bond forces and repulsive nonbonded interactions. They also performed some calculations with no bonds; this represents the case of an ideal fluid of monomers. Simulations involving constant rates of strain were performed to study the effects of variables such as strain rate, density, chain length, and temperature. Because the representation of the molecular system was simple, the simulation history could be interpreted in great detail. In keeping with other findings, they concluded that shear stress was primarily due to excluded volume interactions (i.e., nonbonded forces) rather than to covalent forces. A plot showing the two contributions is reproduced as Fig. 6.6. The horizontal axis is time, during which the strain grows at a constant rate, and the vertical axis is the contribution to the shear stress. The important result of chain continuity, as shown by comparing the simulations with and without bonding forces, is to reduce atomic mobility and thus to slow the rate of accommodation to the imposed stress.

It should be emphasized that while model simplification may facilitate computations and interpretation, it may also have consequences for the quantitative validity of the results. As a relevant example we note the comparison of extended-atom and all-atom models in simulations of polymethylene chains by Yoon et al. [108]. Chain conformations were adequately reproduced by the all-atom simulations, but other properties, such as orientational order, were not. To evaluate the effects of model parameters on dynamic properties, the authors monitored the mean-square displacement of the chain center of mass as a function of time. The slope of this plot is the effective diffusion coefficient. Inclusion of all atoms reduced these coefficients by a

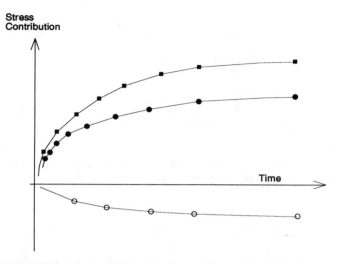

Figure 6.6 Simulated contributions to the shear stress in a polymer melt (see Ref. 109). —O—O—O— **Covalent.** —■—■—■— **Non-covalent.** —●—●—●— **Total.**

factor of 6 to 8, bringing them into agreement with experimental values. In the next chapter we will see additional examples of such dramatic changes; the one cited here is not an isolated result, but rather seems to express correctly the sensitive dependence of some properties on the presence of explicit hydrogen atoms in the model. Since mechanical properties in the melt involve diffusive behavior, it is important to bear in mind this dependence of simulated results on details of the model.

6.6   Ultimate Properties

Not discussed thus far in this chapter is the question of extreme stresses, which lead to failure of the material. In polymers, three modes of failure are recognized: creep failure, due to stresses applied for a long period of time; fatigue failure, due to repeated application of cyclic stresses; and environmental stress cracking, in which attacking solvents or other conditions, either by themselves or combined with mechanical stress, produce failure.

The phenomenology of polymer ultimate properties can be simply summarized by the different examples of stress-strain curves, such as those shown in Fig. 6.7. Hard, brittle materials show little elongation at break, but require large stresses; tough materials are characterized by large elongations at break, with large requirements of work-to-break, as indicated by the area under the stress-strain curve. Weak, soft materials break with less work imposed, and at lower elongations.

We have reviewed calculations of ultimate properties only for directions perpendicular to crystalline orientations. These can be done with relatively less computation

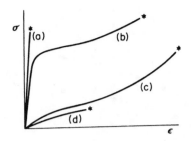

Figure 6.7. Stress-strain curves to breakage (denoted by *) for four types of materials: (a) hard, brittle; (b) hard, tough; (c) soft, tough; (d) soft, weak. Compare to curves in Fig. 6.4.

than would be necessary for the complete simulation of stress-strain curves. The only case study reviewed here for amorphous polymers was the work of Brown and Clarke [99] in which high rates of deformation were used. The stress-strain curves show obvious yield points at about 20% elongation (refer to Fig. 6.4). The change from elastic response to plastic flow is most clear for lower temperatures, and above about 300 K there is no clear differentiation of the behavior based on elongation. In fact, if the tension at 20% elongation is plotted against temperature, it extrapolates to zero at around 400 K; this can be used a measure of the glass transition temperature.

An interesting fact of polymer ultimate strength is that measured values are only about one-fifth of what would be obtained if all the main-chain bonds had to be broken, as described in Ref. [96]. On the other hand, for tearing of crystalline polymers, as in Refs. [104] and [105], the tear merely separates parallel chains, and nonbonded forces appear to give a good account of the strength of the material. It was these observations that first led to concepts of material separation by pulling chains past one another rather than breaking them. Breaking of materials is believed to proceed by means of small local defects, with a small tear serving to concentrate stresses and allow propagation of the defects; examples of computational simulations starting from this idea are a simple treatment of a gel consisting only of bonded interactions [109] and a calculation of the weakening of metals that takes place in hydrogen embrittlement [110]. In the context of polymers, it would be expected that near the tear boundary, reptation of a single chain or a few chains from within the material could be simulated with a relatively small model in which forces are applied to chain ends, and the mechanisms of reptation observed.

6.7   Summary

In this Chapter we reviewed applications of molecular modeling to the motions and mechanisms responsible for the mechanical properties of polymers. As in the case of structural modeling discussed in the previous Chapter, useful information can be obtained from the study of single polymer chains and how they respond to axial stretching. In more realistic multi-chain material models, the external mechanical stimulus analogous to chain stretching is the deformation of a periodic box; different deformations correspond to uniform compression, uniaxial tension, and shear. The response of the model material to the deformation is simulated using energy minimization or molecular dynamics; the moduli and mechanisms can be extracted from the results. Application of this methodology at different temperatures produces behavior ranging from elastic response to viscoelastic flow. Because of limitations in computer resources, the simulations often must be very fast on the molecular time scale; the model may not have time to respond fully to the deformations. Some work in which the rate of applied tension was varied indicates how the results are dependent on this simulation condition.

A related field of study is the elucidation of the microscopic details of the response mechanisms. The environment of individual groups can be examined using molecular mechanics, and the energetics of assumed relaxation mechanisms, such as ring rotation or functional group deformation, can be calculated, following procedures which have been developed for studies on relaxation mechanisms in the interior of globular proteins.

Calculations of the types described here can be applied to amorphous systems below or above the glass transition or melting temperatures, as well as to crystalline polymers. The perfect crystal is a limiting case, never fully realized in polymeric materials, which can be treated with analytical procedures to provide results for comparison with the simulation approaches. The melt is a state in which all order is lost; it can be studied with simpler models such as spheres or lattice models to obtain general characteristics that should apply to many melted polymers. Finally, several approaches to the simulation of ultimate behavior have been sketched out. As more experience with these methods is gained, and as computers continue to become faster and more available, considerable progress should take place in this field.

7

Diffusion, Surface Phenomena, and Energy Transfer

In this chapter we examine methods for modeling phenomena that depend in a more complicated fashion on structure, especially on the dynamic aspects of structure. While the title may appear to represent an unusual collection of topics, they are actually interrelated in that they are mediated by microscopic-level motions and relaxation processes. All of these aspects of polymer behavior can be interpreted at the atomistic level, and should be candidates for study and elucidation by modern simulation methods.

The diffusion of small molecules in polymers is experimentally measured as the permeability, which is the product of the solubility and the diffusion coefficient. The fundamental property of interest is the diffusion coefficient, and recent simulations have begun to be capable of yielding quantitatively accurate results. The concentration of penetrant present in a polymer is the amount dissolved, which is proportional to the external pressure or chemical potential, plus the amount adsorbed, which follows a Langmuir-type isotherm as a function of pressure. Solubility is another fundamental property which should be available from simulations. The surface phenomena of adsorption, wetting, and coating, are of commercial interest; this includes both coatings on polymer substrates (as in multi-layer materials) and coatings of polymers of other materials such as metals.

All of these phenomena involve internal dynamic processes such as local density fluctuations and energy transfer. These processes are also important in accounting for the properties and responses of polymers to mechanical stresses and environmental attack by solvents, high temperature, or other agents such as ionizing radiation. Thus the topics in this chapter all depend on microscopic dynamic processes, and they all represent a step toward problems of commercial and industrial importance and beyond "simple" questions of structure (complicated though these may be at the detailed level). The purpose of this chapter is to indicate the extent to which the detailed, atomistic computational approach can account for these phenomena, and where the shortcomings and topics for future research remain.

In the discussion of diffusion we will be primarily concerned with the mobility within amorphous polymers of small penetrant molecules such as common atmospheric gases. Brief consideration will be given also to larger, irregularly shaped molecules such as plasticizers. As indicated, there is a component of adsorption influencing the concentration of gases in polymers, and in this connection we will briefly review theoretical studies of the surfaces of polymers, terminating both in the vacuum and at boundaries with other materials. This will set the stage for discussion of the other surface phenomena mentioned, such as wetting, coatings, polymer films, and interdiffusion, including a brief look at questions of compatibility and solubility. Finally the topic of energy transfer sums up this section on the dynamic nature of polymer structure; one example simulation of a problem of practical interest, flammability, will be examined.

7.1   Diffusion in Polymers

One of the earliest qualitative discussions of gas diffusion in polymers accompanied the measurements of Meares [111], who proposed a model in which the gas molecules jump between voids that are spontaneously created by thermal fluctuations of the polymer matrix. This idea qualitatively accounts for the gradual increase in diffusion with temperature and the large increase as the temperature rises above the glass transition temperature. Though put forth nearly forty years ago, the void-jump model has been substantially borne out by detailed simulations, which offer additional insight into the microscopic structural details involved.

A mechanistic model based on the idea of a spherical penetrant confined by a parallel bundle of polymer chains was advanced by Brandt [112] and DiBenedetto [113] and evaluated statistically by DiBenedetto and Paul [114]. In this model the diffusivity depends on fluctuations which create voids that allow the penetrant to move either parallel or perpendicular to the bundle of chains. An elaboration of this model which allows evaluation based on a small number of adjustable parameters with simple physical interpretations was carried out by Pace and Daytner for spherical [115] and non-spherical penetrants [116].

The direct atomistic simulation of small molecule diffusion within macromolecules first was proposed and carried out in a context quite different from the present consideration of polymers. The issue arose during modeling studies of heme proteins [117] which are carriers of oxygen to working tissues. Apart from mechanistic questions about the cooperative oxygen uptake and release process, there arose the observation that a definite void existed to accommodate the oxygen molecule at its binding site, but that in general, proteins did not possess such voids. The problem was to understand how the oxygen moved from outside the heme protein to its binding site at the heme iron, which is buried within the folded globin chain.

Straightforward testing for voids, by placing an oxygen molecule at each point of a regular cubic grid around and inside one hemoglobin unit, showed that there were few voids, they were small, and any channels leading from the surface to the heme were significantly constricted. The diffusion of oxygen into the binding site would therefore be an activated process with a large barrier, and this could not be reconciled with the evident rapid uptake and release rates. The resolution of this apparent paradox lies in consideration of thermal motions which create fluctuations in the void structure of the globin and permit the oxygen to hop from void to void with very low activation energy barriers. The process was first simulated with molecular dynamics in 1979 [118], using a single oxygen particle; newer techniques have been developed to obtain enhanced sampling and reduce the computational requirements by simultaneously following the trajectories of multiple gas particles [119]. In this chapter we review similar techniques as they have been applied to the problem of diffusion in polymeric substances.

The microscopic definition of the self-diffusion coefficient is a simple formulation related to the motion of a particle over time:

$$\langle |R(t) - R(0)|^2 \rangle = 6Dt$$

where $R(t)$ is a position vector for the particle at time t, the angle brackets indicate an average over time, and D is the diffusion coefficient, in units of length^2/time (e.g., cm^2/sec). In the processing of simulation data, the mean square displacement is plotted as a function of time elapsed in the simulation, and D is extracted as 1/6 of the slope of a best-fit line. The position vector itself undergoes jumps, or abrupt transitions, corresponding to a hop from one void to another. The corresponding velocity vector would be relatively small in magnitude except when the particle moves during collisions or jumps.

That diffusion is an activated process shown by the thermal dependence of the diffusion coefficient; experimentally, it closely fits the Arrhenius form

$$D = D_0 \exp(-E_A/kT)$$

where the pre-exponential factor D_0 is a fundamental parameter that depends on the details of the system, and E_A is the apparent activation energy. In simple physical terms, higher temperature increases the mobility of the polymer chains and increases the likelihood of fluctuations leading to voids and channels through which the penetrant molecule can move.

A gas which is confined over a polymer sample will diffuse into the material, reaching a concentration dependent on the pressure. Empirically, the concentration of the dissolved gas is

$$c_p = Sp + Cbp/(1 + bp)$$

where c_p is the molarity of penetrant at vapor pressure p over the polymer; S is the definition of solubility, and the second term, with parameters C and b, is a Langmuir-type isotherm for sorption of gas particles onto specific sites.

Simulations designed to obtain values for the diffusion coefficient are now straightforward, though exacting in their details and computationally intensive. Repeating such a simulation at different temperatures can produce the Arrhenius constants. One method of evaluating the solubility is the so-called *test-particle insertion* method, in which a particle is inserted at a randomly chosen position within the polymer matrix and its energy evaluated. This is repeated for many particles, and for many instances of the polymer matrix (e.g., a series of snapshots from a molecular dynamics simulation), until sufficient data are available to obtain converged averages. Repeated simulations at various penetrant concentrations provide another means to determine the solubility and isotherm parameters.

It is apparent that even the simplest of these simulations requires a considerable amount of work. First, a good material model has to be built and equilibrated, and as we have seen, this process itself can involve a significant amount of computer simulation. Some attention needs to be paid to the initial conditions of the diffusion simulation, including number and placement of penetrant molecules, and degree of equilibration of the polymer model. After insertion of the penetrants, a re-equilibration may be required because the penetrants may have been placed in small voids, causing large nonbonded repulsions. The system is then ready for the diffusion simulation, which typically must cover at least 50 psec; most of the work reviewed here involved much longer simulation times. Finally, the results are extracted from an analysis of the trajectories. Detailed examination of polymer motions involved in jump mechanisms can require additional calculations, such as the construction of geometric figures defining voids and channels.

7.1.1 Simulation of Diffusion Mechanism

As a first example we review a series of simulations by Takeuchi, Okazaki, Roe, and Mark. In the first of these [120] a relatively simple model of amorphous polyethylene was constructed from chains of 20 extended atoms, where each extended atom represented a methylene $-CH_2-$ group of mass 14 amu (or $-CH_3$, mass 15, for end groups). The motion of these spherical segments was governed by a valence force field with terms for bond stretching, valence angle bending, torsions, and nonbonded (van der Waals) interactions. In a separate simulation, the polymer was made more flexible by omission of the torsional potentials. The penetrant was oxygen, represented by a sphere of mass 32 and an appropriate radius, interacting with polymer units only through nonbonded forces.

The polymeric material model consisted of 30 chains (for a total of 600 carbons) which were built by an amorphous growth procedure that permitted approach of nonbonded atoms to within 80% of the sum of van der Waals radii. Extensive energy minimization and dynamics equilibration were used to produce the relaxed starting material. 20 penetrant molecules were inserted, followed by additional equilibration. A diagram of the model system is shown in Fig. 7.1.

Then five data collection runs of approximately 200 psec each were conducted at temperatures well above the glass transition temperature. The diffusion behavior was that of a simple liquid, with clear Arrhenius-type temperature dependence and a low activation energy of only a few kcal/mol. For the more flexible chain (without torsional forces) the higher mobility was clearly evident, but the differences were not great; the fluctuation behavior was determined more by packing than by detailed chain dynamics.

The very high mobility (low activation energy) derived from this simulation led the investigators to alter the polymer model to reduce the large fraction of free chain ends, which likely contribute to an increased mobility within the material [121]. T_g of the model was determined by two different methods (essentially one heating and one cooling) as 154 and 190 K, and the simulations were done at about 120 K, instead of well above T_g as in the previous calculation. 10 penetrant molecules were inserted and the behavior analyzed. As expected from the more rigid model and especially

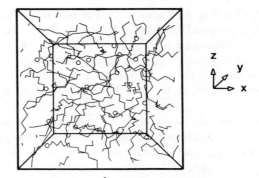

Figure 7.1. Equilibrated sample prepared for simulation of gaseous diffusion in a short-chain amorphous polymer. The box is reproduced with periodic boundary conditions. Open circles represent the penetrant gas molecules. Reprinted with permission from Ref. 120. Copyright 1990 American Institute of Physics.

from the lower temperature, most of the behavior consisted of small oscillations as the penetrants remained trapped in small, local voids. One case of jumping to a new void was analyzed in detail. The displacement history for the jumping oxygen molecule is contrasted with that of a confined molecule in Fig. 7.2.

Potential energy surfaces for the mobile penetrant were calculated for snapshot configurations of the polymer before, during, and after the jump; they clearly show the formation of a new cavity, the creation of a channel connecting it to the cavity occupied by the penetrant, and finally the annihilation of the original cavity. The changing shapes of the interaction potentials surrounding the oxygen molecule are depicted in the ten snapshots of Fig. 7.3. The nonbonded energy experienced by one

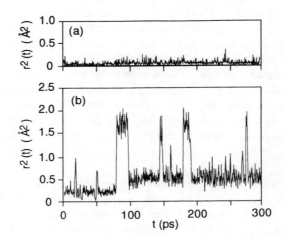

Figure 7.2. Simulated displacement *vs.* time during a 300-psec molecular dynamics simulation for (a) trapped oxygen molecule and (b) oxygen molecule which executes jumps. Reprinted with permission from Ref. 121. Copyright 1990 American Institute of Physics.

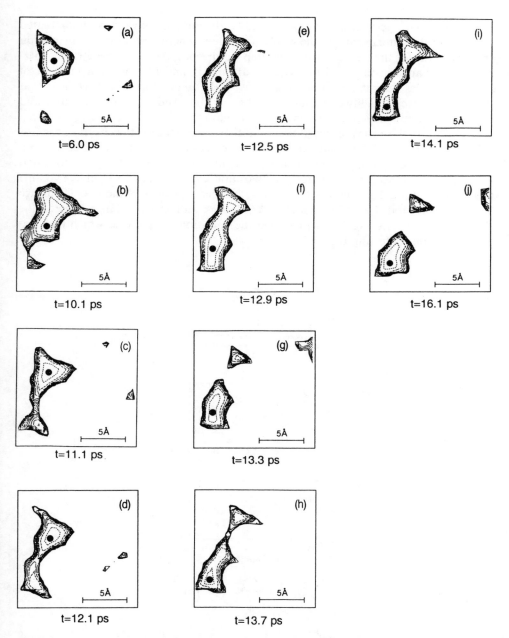

Figure 7.3. The potential energy experienced by the oxygen molecule during its jump. Contour intervals are 50 kJ/mol (11.95 kcal/mol). The dot shows the current position of the oxygen molecule. In frame (a) the molecule is localized in a void. Frames (c) and (d) show the formation of a channel connecting to a newly formed void. In frames (e), (f), and (g) the oxygen molecule jumps to the new void and the channel closes. Although the channel re-opens in frames (h) and (i), the oxygen molecule does not jump back to its original void. Reprinted with permission from Ref. 121. Copyright 1990 American Institute of Physics.

of the trapped oxygens, and that experienced by the jumping oxygen, both fluctuated throughout the jump event and the whole simulation. There is no obvious correlation or coincidence of this energy with the jump occurrence. Also, the penetrant experienced no change in the local free volume around it, and the torsional motions of chain molecules near it were uncorrelated with the jump (Fig. 7.4). It is clear that the jump involves a highly cooperative mechanism, but its details are not simple and remained incompletely elucidated by this simulation.

Continuing this series of simulations, another paper studied the effects of the free volume distribution [122]. The model was once again ten penetrant molecules in a material of 600 carbons, with no chain ends. Diffusion behavior at 300 K was found to correlate with the average interchain separation, even when the overall free volume was held constant. The chains were built with different values of the C-C-C valence angle, namely, 100, 110, 130, and 150°. While this geometrical change affected the chain dynamics only slightly, it produced the variations in packing which changed the free volume, affecting the diffusion behavior.

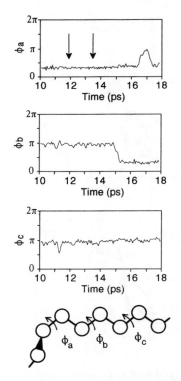

Figure 7.4. Conformational changes in the polymer chain closest to the jumping oxygen molecule. The jump occurs between the times marked by the two arrows in the upper graph. The large conformational change which occurs after $T = 15$ psec is not correlated with the jump, which occurs during a period of small fluctuations. Reprinted with permission from Ref. 121. Copyright 1990 American Institute of Physics.

7.1.2   Factors Affecting Quantitative Accuracy

In a series of papers on diffusion in amorphous polyethylene and polypropylene, Müller-Plathe [123–127] sought to elucidate the details of the diffusion mechanism and to evaluate factors that affected the quantitative agreement between calculated and experimental diffusion coefficients. In the first simulation [123], 20 chains of 50 spherical extended atoms each were packed amorphously by assigning a 0.6 probability to the *trans* state and 0.2 to each of the *gauche* states. Significant amounts of molecular dynamics were used to equilibrate the material both before and after the insertion of 20 penetrant methane molecules. The displacement history of several of the methanes is shown in Fig. 7.5. The diffusion coefficient obtained was approximately two orders of magnitude larger than experimental measurements. One source of error noted (apart from inadequacies in the model or the simulation conditions) was the lack of crystallinity in the model; crystallinity is known to reduce diffusion, most likely because of the closer chain packing in crystalline regions. Portions of the simulation were repeated with the gas-polymer interaction reduced by factors of ten and 100. It was found that the hopping mechanism as just described above still holds, but there are simply more hops per unit time, and overall greater mobility of the penetrant molecules.

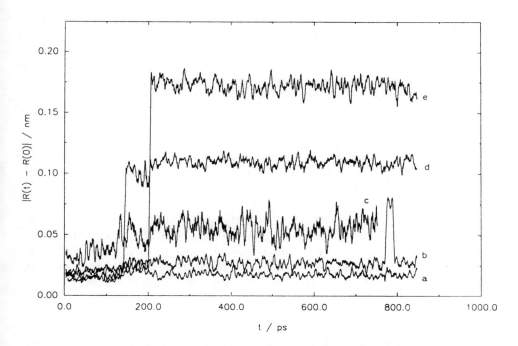

Figure 7.5. Displacement of several methane molecules in the course of a molecular dynamics simulation. Reprinted with permission from Ref. 123. Copyright 1991 American Institute of Physics.

In a second simulation [124], Müller-Plathe compared the solubility and adsorption isotherm constants for helium, hydrogen, nitrogen, oxygen, and methane in amorphous polypropylene. Molecular dynamics was used in conjunction with the test particle insertion method mentioned above to calculate the solubility. Although it is the largest molecule, methane is the most soluble; helium is small and has high diffusivity, but is relatively insoluble.

A third simulation [125] was conducted to try to eliminate factors that led to quantitative errors. For example, some explicit hydrogens were included (instead of using extended atoms for all of the model); chain ends were eliminated by folding one long chain rather than building the carbon-equivalent number of short chains; and the initial amorphous geometry obtained had the correct density. The problem of introducing microcrystallites could not be addressed, but by studying atactic polypropylene, a truly amorphous material, this consideration should be eliminated and the simulation results should be directly comparable to experimental data. The simulation was carried out with eight molecules of H_2 or O_2, or with ten molecules of methane. Hydrogen was found to be about ten times more mobile than oxygen (the calculated diffusion coefficients were 43.5×10^{-6} cm^2/sec and 4.04×10^{-6} respectively), and eighty times more than methane (0.479×10^{-6}). The only experimental diffusion coefficient available was for H_2, and was about eight times smaller than the simulated result. Estimates for O_2 and CH_4 from diffusion measurements in natural and synthetic rubber were closer to the calculated values, with surprisingly close agreement for CH_4. Remaining sources of error are assessed: they include the accuracy of the interaction potentials (energy functions), and variations in the actual materials (due to origin and processing) leading to a range of experimental values. Overall, agreement within an order of magnitude was considered good. Of special value for modeling studies was the apparent correctness of the order of results, suggesting that even if quantitatively precise values cannot be obtained, it should be possible to determine through simulation which materials will be more and less permeable.

Further exploring the effects of model parameters, Müller-Plathe and colleagues directly compared simulation results from models built with extended atoms and all atoms [126]. Two sets of nonbonded parameters for the oxygen penetrant were compared for the extended-atom simulations. The conclusion of the paper is reflected by its positive title: *Diffusion coefficients of penetrant gases in polyisobutylene can be calculated correctly by molecular dynamics simulations.* The experimental diffusion coefficient for oxygen in polyisobutylene is 0.081×10^{-6} cm^2/sec. The extended-atom simulations produced values in the range of 2.5 to 8.2×10^{-6} (i.e., 30 to 100 times too large), while the all-atom simulation yielded 0.169×10^{-6}, only a factor of two too large. The authors rationalize the results with a packing argument. The density of the simulated polymer was the same, regardless of whether extended atoms or all atoms were used; the extended-atom radii are adjusted to produce this result. Therefore the difference must be due to the geometry of the voids: the larger number of small spheres in the all-atom model leaves a larger number of smaller interstitial voids, and the rate of diffusion is reduced. In the earlier work with larger penetrants in materials such as polyethylene and polypropylene, which have less closely packed structures, the extended atom model was more nearly applicable. This accounts for the fortuitous result mentioned above for CH_4 in atactic polypropylene.

In further studies with the all-atom model of polyisobutylene [127], Müller-Plathe and colleagues computed diffusion coefficients for He and H_2 using both the standard dynamics method considered so far, and a new non-equilibrium dynamics method. In the latter, the penetrant is dragged through the polymer network by an external force. For He the experimental diffusion coefficient is 5.63 (in units of 10^{-6} cm^2/sec), while the value from equilibrium molecular dynamics was 30.1; the non-equilibrium method gave 52.8. For H_2, the figures are: experimental 1.52, equilibrium MD 4.0 (the non-equilibrium method was not used for H_2). For O_2, the non-equilibrium method gave a value of 0.57, or about three times larger than the result reviewed in the previous paragraph.

Evidently the standard molecular dynamics method still overestimates the diffusion coefficient for very small penetrants, while the non-equilibrium method pulls the penetrant too forcefully through the medium. Systematic aspects, such as the size of the model polymer network, the details of its microstructure, and the force fields, may be at the root of the remaining discrepancies. This series of papers shows nevertheless the advances that have been made in recent years in achieving quantitatively useful results.

7.1.3   Other Simulations of Small-Molecule Diffusion

While the discussion thus far has made clear the general outlines of methodology for evaluation of gas diffusion in polymers, we recount some additional examples in this section, either for additional interesting points of technique or for their value as practical applications.

7.1.3.1 Contrasts in Chemically Isomeric Polymers

Boyd and Krishna Pant [128] confronted the experimental observation that polyisobutylene (PIB) has a rate of gas diffusion approximately 5 to 10 times smaller than the chemically isomeric polyethylene. (Müller-Plathe et al. further pointed out that the pair of polymers polyvinyl chloride and polyvinylidene chloride are analogous to polypropylene and polyisobutylene, with the chlorines replaced by methyl groups. The gas permeability contrast is the same for both pairs.) Simple mechanistic considerations would suggest that PIB must have better packing, despite the pendant methyl groups; indeed, its density is higher than that of polyethylene. The interesting model-building procedure used in this paper has been reviewed in Chapter 4; it consists of starting with an ordered crystal, and changing the system by reptation-like moves in which a group is removed from one end of a chain and "grown" on the other end in one of the stereochemically allowed isomeric states. After a large number of such steps, the system achieves an amorphous nature and is prepared for the diffusion simulations through energy minimization and molecular dynamics equilibration. Qualitatively, the polyethylene chains act as thin tubes with roughness at kinks or bends; PIB is in effect a thicker, but still smooth tube — the extra methyl sidegroup does not really protrude — which achieves slightly better packing. The diffusion simulation results in numbers which are of the right order (diffusion is slower in PIB than in PE) but considerably too high.

Rather than resorting to an all-atom description, Krishna Pant and Boyd obtained improved results by examining the shortcomings of the united atom potentials. Beginning with polyethylene [129], they observed that the united atom potentials produced a material with too low a density. Equivalently, in a constant-volume simulation, the material was actually under a negative pressure; the structure seen by the penetrant was too open and thus the diffusion coefficients were too high. To rectify the situation, these authors employed an "anisotropic united atom" potential due to Toxvaerd [130] in which the nonbonded potential is no longer centered on the carbon position of the united atom, but displaced in the direction of the hydrogens. The potentials are further calibrated to give the proper pressure-temperature-volume behavior. The results with polyethylene were striking: conventional atom-centered all-atom potentials gave diffusion coefficients for methane of 1.2×10^{-9} m^2/sec (for C_{24} chains) and 0.7×10^{-9} (for a model with no chain ends), while the anisotropic united atom potential yielded 0.049×10^{-9} for a model with no chain ends. Experimental diffusion coefficients for methane in polyethylene samples of varying crystallinity and branching are in the range of 0.030 to 0.060×10^{-9} m^2/sec.

Proceeding to the comparison between polyethylene and polyisobutylene, Krishna Pant and Boyd again employed anisotropic united atom potentials; this time the different carbon environments were calibrated separately [131]. Numerical results were not quoted, but rather shown on plots of log D versus 1000/T. It was evident that the simulation results were as close to a best-fit curve as the experimental points; equivalently, the differences among experimental measurements were similar to the deviations of the calculated results from the best-fit curve. The coefficients for polyisobutylene were six to eight times lower than those for polyethylene. This simulation appears to have been equally as successful as those of Müller-Plathe et al. in achieving quantitative accuracy.

7.1.3.2 Permeability of Polymer Membranes

Sok, Berendsen, and van Gunsteren [132] calculated diffusion coefficients for helium and methane in polydimethylsiloxane. They phrased the problem in terms of permeability and diffusion through a membrane, but the simulation methods are the same as described above. If the diffusion constant is D and the solubility factor s, then the permeability P is defined as the product $s \cdot D$. P is also defined in terms of the flux J through a membrane of thickness d due to a concentration difference Δc; $J = P \cdot (\Delta c)/d$ (Fick's law).

In this problem five chains of 30 monomers each were built up with a distribution of torsion angles, then equilibrated through energy minimization and molecular dynamics. The diffusion simulations show the same jump mechanism as seen in other studies. Helium jumps so frequently that it is essentially freely diffusing, whereas methane has a residence time of about 25 psec, which is much longer than the average lifetime of cavities. Again the results are within approximately order-of-magnitude correctness. Fig. 7.6 shows the trajectories of a methane molecule (for 250 psec) and a helium atom (for 150 psec). The methane can be seen to jump from one localized region to another. From analysis of the trajectory, the jump occurs in less than a picosecond. Drawings of the free volumes in the plane of the jump show that a tunnel spontaneously opens, permitting the methane to move.

An interesting practical application of polymer material engineering has occurred in the development of contact lenses made of polymethylmethacrylate (PMMA). This material has a low oxygen permeability and is known to be associated with corneal irritation. The oxygen permeability has been improved by copolymerizing MMA with tris-trimethoxysiloxy silylpropyl methacrylate (TRIS). The attractive possibility exists of using simulation techniques to determine the optimum TRIS fraction to promote oxygen permeability, and also to understand the changes in structure due to copolymerization and the molecular mechanisms leading to increased permeability. This is just one example of such practical applications where the cooperation of theory, simulation, and experimental work can improve problem-solving ability.

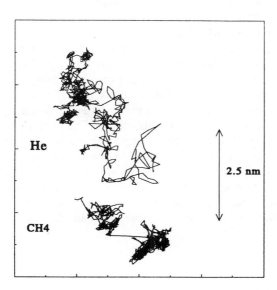

Figure 7.6. Trajectories of one methane molecule (for 250 psec) and one helium atom (for 150 psec) in polydimethylsiloxane. The helium is essentially freely diffusing, while the methane makes several discrete jumps. Reprinted with permission from Ref. 132. Copyright 1991 American Institute of Physics.

7.1.4   Diffusion of Larger Molecules

Related to the question of gas diffusion is the problem of the motion of larger species within polymeric materials. Interest in this topic arises both from a desire to introduce external materials, such as plasticizers, and to understand phenomena such as exudation of unpolymerized or partly polymerized material. Aside from possible effects on mechanical properties, the latter has obvious significance for building materials and their effects on the environment experienced by residents or office workers.

Clearly the behavior will be different from that of gases which can easily find cavities of sufficient size to exist and migrate within polymeric materials. Here we wish to consider added molecules which, though still relatively small, are many times larger than gases and the voids present in polymeric materials, and which have irregular geometries that cannot be approximated as spheres, ellipsoids, etc. The problem was first treated by Pace and Daytner [116] who generalized from a small spherical penetrant to one that was elongated, but still small (i.e., similar to the dimensions of polymer voids). A more recent approach to the subject was made by Coughlin *et al.* [133], although they did not attempt to carry out detailed molecular dynamics simulations. They formulated the problem in terms of principal axes of the introduced species, and obtained a theory in which the diffusion coefficient is the average of the three diffusion coefficients which correspond to unit hopping displacements in the directions of the principal axes. This unit displacement is only a fraction of the characteristic dimension. Among the interesting observations reported is the fact that for a given molecular volume, the more compact species diffuses more *slowly* than an extended or irregularly-shaped one.

Conceptually, it is not difficult to formulate a simulation strategy for this problem, but it might be difficult to develop an approach that could be evaluated without excessive computing requirements. An initial problem is how to introduce the large penetrant into the material model. If it is simply placed arbitrarily, or even in the largest cavity in the model, there will be many large nonbonded repulsions, which will require a great deal of energy minimization and molecular dynamics before the material returns to equilibrium. Such an approach might also introduce unwanted systematic alterations of the polymer model (in effect, re-crystallization of the model around the penetrant). Another approach would be to pull the penetrant into the surface of the polymer using an artificial force on all the penetrant atoms, similar to the non-equilibrium molecular dynamics technique referenced above [127]. This would allow the penetrant to take advantage of fortuitous fluctuations and to enter the polymer network gradually.

7.2   Polymer Surface Structure

Consideration thus far has been limited to the uniform, semi-infinite interior of polymer materials, and the phenomena that take place within this phase. A science of surface studies has emerged because surfaces are associated with their own special phenomena, reflecting the fact that the surface of a material is different from its interior. In the polymer context, a descriptive account of a variety of surface phenomena can be obtained from the book of Clark and Feast [134]. More recently, several simulation studies have been directed at elucidation of the difference between polymer surfaces and the bulk material, and we begin with them before considering some applications of surface phenomena.

In the chapter on polymer structure we alluded to two models of crystallites. The earlier fringed micelle model envisioned chains passing through many individual crystalline regions, while the later and currently accepted model features single chains repeatedly folding, each upon itself, to form many parallel and anti-parallel strands. Similarly, one could visualize the polymer surface as a planar boundary where all the chains end, or where they turn back within the polymer.

Mansfield and Theodorou [135] constructed a model of an infinite slab of material built up from a unit cell approximately 61 Å thick, with vacuum above and below, and with a square cross-section of about 17×17 Å. They built their material by an amorphous-growth procedure, using a model with five rotational states and building three chains of 76 monomers each of atactic polypropylene. A special "wall" potential was included to keep the chains growing within the box. A three-step energy minimization process then generated the final microstate; the three steps involved energy minimization with differing nonbonded potentials, until finally the full nonbonded potential could be used. This is the same technique used by Theodorou and Suter in their study of the amorphous state, reviewed in Chapters 4 and 5 [64]. Twenty such structures were generated, and these formed the ensemble for the statistical evaluations of the material and surface properties.

The effect of the surface on structure was two-fold in this model. First, there was a density gradient which began almost 5 Å from the surface, as the density fell from the model-built value of 0.892 g/cm^3 within the material to approximately zero at the surface (Fig. 7.7). Secondly, near the surface the main-chain bonds tended to be oriented parallel to the surface, while in the bulk material they were randomly oriented. The interpretation is that the surface enhances the effective local crystallinity, accounting for an increase in density *above* the bulk value for a thin layer a few ångstroms from the surface.

In a sense, this work anticipated the surface phenomena by including a surface tension-like force in the model. The artificial "wall" potential was designed only to keep the growing chains within the surface boundary, but probably, as the density in the interior of the material increased during the model-building procedure, the effect was to force the chains to lie along the surface. Whether this model is correct in detail may be decided in the near future by new forms of surface microscopy [136, 137].

The same authors repeated their work for the case of a polymeric material terminating at a semi-infinite plane of solid [138]. Here two graphite planes were placed about 72 Å apart, and the polymer was built into unit cells whose projections on the graphite surfaces measured about 25×25 Å. Some 15 systems were constructed at this size, and 35 were built to a smaller size. Averaging over these microstates produced the statistical picture of the material. The boundary effects

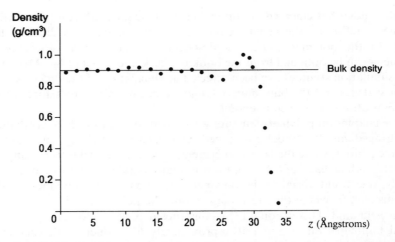

Figure 7.7. Simulated variation of polymer density from the interior (z = 0) to the polymer-vacuum interface (z = 30 ångstroms).

began over 10 Å from the surface, and the density rose to a local maximum at the graphite interface, where the chains tended to line up parallel to the surface with a high percentage of *trans* states.

In contrast to these studies of solid polymer material, others have considered dilute or semi-dilute polymer solutions and their behavior near hard walls. Such systems are of obvious importance in polymer processing and engineering, but are beyond the scope of detailed atomistic simulations. More schematic calculations, such as Monte Carlo simulations of lattice models, have been the main approaches. The phenomenology of these systems is not well known; it is thought that there is a depletion of polymer concentration within approximately one characteristic length, i.e., one polymer dimension, of the wall. An example of this type of simulation is the work of Shih *et al.* [139], which arrived at quantitative relationships for the size of the correlation length and radius of gyration as functions of concentration.

7.3   Surface Interactions

The rationale for developing models of polymer surfaces, apart from the fundamental study of this aspect of structure, is to use them to study applications of surface phenomena such as wetting, adsorption, and solubility. In the examples discussed here we will encounter surface models different from those mentioned in the previous section. The emphasis is on the simulation methods and models; it is to be hoped that further experimental observations and additional calculations will help discriminate among different models and indicate which ones are most appropriate for the various types of calculation.

7.3.1   Wetting of Polymer Surfaces

The phenomenon of wetting involves the spreading of a liquid droplet on a surface to the point where its surface tension, which tends to hold a droplet spherical when it is in free space, balances the molecular attraction between the liquid and the surface. Wetting is measured either by droplet spreading or contact angle, and a polymer surface can be characterized by obtaining these measurements for a standard series of known liquids [134].

The molecular interactions in this phenomenon are highly amenable to molecular dynamics simulation. Once the polymer surface is constructed and equilibrated, either by the elaborate methods discussed in the previous section or otherwise, a micro-droplet of the equilibrated solvent is placed near enough to the surface so that nonbonded forces between liquid and polymer take effect and produce the behavior of interest in the simulation. Droplet sizes of approximately 20 Å are convenient, because they are large enough to have an interior dominated by solvent–solvent interactions, and because the number of molecules required to make a sphere of that size is not too large. Fig. 7.8 diagrams the simulation model.

In addition to a full simulation of all the particles and interactions in this system, two levels of computational simplification can be considered. Since the polymer is pre-equilibrated and has reached an average structure, the details of the polymer motions may be of lesser interest, and the polymer may be "frozen." This affords a major reduction of computing effort; the problem becomes that of a group of solvent molecules evolving in the presence of their own (solvent–solvent) and external (solvent–polymer) interactions. A still more schematic simulation could be done by assuming a structureless polymer substrate, with the liquid-polymer interaction depending in a simple manner on the perpendicular distance of a liquid molecule from the surface [140]. This is obviously not an appropriate model if there are interesting functional groups on the surface which could exert strong interactions on solvent molecules (e.g., polar functional groups interacting with water).

Both the extent and the rate of spreading of the liquid will depend on the nature of the substances and on the details of the polymer-liquid interactions. The length

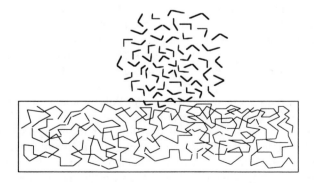

Figure 7.8. Model system for simulation of water droplet wetting a periodic box of polymer surface.

to which the simulation must be carried, therefore, can only be determined by observing the behavior and continuing the calculations until a steady state is reached. Liquids which wet the surface and spread indefinitely will require long enough simulation to assure that limiting behavior has been reached.

7.3.2   Polymer Coatings

Analogous to the wetting of a polymer surface by a liquid is the problem of adherence of a polymer sample to some other, non-polymer surface; the situation of polymers coating a polymer substrate is considered separately in the next section. Polymer coatings on metals are of economic importance, and the details of the polymer-surface bonding can be investigated by simulations. Naturally, these details as revealed by simulation will depend on the model of molecular-level interactions used.

One mechanism of interest in polymer coatings on a metal surface is adsorption through charge-transfer interactions. An explanation of the charge transfer phenomenon would require electronic calculations, but its effects can be modeled much more simply by placing partial electrostatic charges at sites representing functional groups. The partial charges are one of the necessary ingredients in a calculation (see Chapter 3), but are sometimes left out of calculations on simple polymers such as polyethylene and polypropylene that do not have functional groups with significant charge separation or permanent dipoles.

The partial charges depend on local conformation, but for many purposes can be left constant throughout a simulation, regardless of the conformations through which the functional group evolves. The charges are determined from rule-based methods or electronic calculations (see Chapter 3). Once the charges are assigned to all atoms or functional groups of the polymer and the substrate material, they will influence simulations in which a sample of polymer is started near a surface. Some of the polymer functional groups will be able to re-orient in such a way as to form relatively permanent interactions with surface atoms or groups; others, due to the nature of the polymer structure, will not. Both the number and the strength of these interactions can be used as measures of the polymer's bonding ability. It is highly likely that the atomistic simulations would result in much stronger bonding than is actually achievable, because the atomistic model involves idealized models of both the surface and the polymers; for example, the simulated surface that is easiest to model is a perfectly flat, perfectly crystalline system, whereas real surfaces would be neither perfectly ordered nor perfectly clean (see Fig. 7.9). The polymer model would also be an idealized smooth geometry, while real polymer films would contain microscopic (but large on the simulation scale) holes, folds, and other imperfections that would cause poor bonding in local areas.

Another aspect of the deposition of thin films or monolayers of polymers on a substrate is their mode of deposition and packing, which influences their coverage and uniformity and thus their stability and mechanical properties. To a large extent, this is a consequence of geometric factors, the simplest measure of which is the area per chain in a surface of closely packed units. While it is impractical to determine

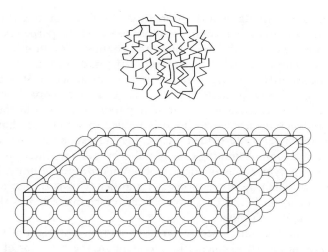

Figure 7.9. Model system for a small droplet of polymer approaching a metal surface.

by simulation the lowest energy conformation of a polymer chain at a surface, it is possible to compare different polymers to determine the relative order of their packing and surface attractions.

The simulation of polymeric chains confined by a surface was discussed above, but in that treatment the chains were not bonded to the surface. An alternative situation is the case in which polymer chains are tethered to the surface to form a brush. An example of the simulation of a polymer brush is the work of Klatte and Beck [141], who performed molecular dynamics on C_8 chains attached to a surface at random positions, but with an excluded area of 20.25 Å^2 (exclusion radius of 4.5 Å per chain). The simulations covered a range of temperatures from 96 to 391 K, at densities up to a maximum of one chain per 41.5 Å^2, the highest experimentally obtained on a chromatographic substrate. The force field contained terms for valence angles, torsions, and nonbonded interactions; each chain was effectively tethered to the surface by making its first atom very heavy. The polymer layer underwent a slow transition from glassy to fluid-like behavior over a broad range of temperature. Torsional transitions in the chains rose from near zero at 200 K and increased steadily with temperature. It is of course difficult to extrapolate from this model with its short 8-carbon chains to one with lengths more characteristic of a real polymeric material, but the simulation methodology should be similar.

7.3.3   Interdiffusion

The next case of interest is the interface between two polymeric materials. The engineering value of such polymer films lies in the possibility of combining unlike materials to obtain desired properties or to mask unwanted ones. For example, a crystalline polymer with high tensile strength in one direction might be coated with a glassy polymer to improve flexibility and properties in the perpendicular direction. At this point we are considering only films and coatings, not an intimate mixture or solution of two materials; that is the subject of the next section.

It is not necessarily the case that two unlike substances will bond well in the thin-film form envisioned for these applications. At a microscopic level, the question is whether there are sufficient intramolecular interactions to hold the two surfaces together. If not, then a mechanical bond is needed in which the chains of the two materials are intimately intertwined. Achieving this state requires a microscopic process of interdiffusion. A limiting case of polymer–polymer interdiffusion is that in which one of the polymers has the degree of polymerization of unity, i.e., where one polymer is being coated by the monomer of another. This is similar to the diffusion problem brought up in Sec. 7.1.4 above. Here we are interested in the diffusion of long chains through each other.

Given the techniques discussed so far, it should be a straightforward extension, though certainly not a trivial calculation, to simulate the behavior of such a system with molecular dynamics. The question is whether calculations long enough to observe meaningful interactions are practicable. The motions of interest are reptation of the chains from each domain across the interface and into the other, and these are processes of a duration that is long compared to molecular dynamics time steps. At the end of this section, we review one calculation which shows that such motions can indeed be simulated, although the calculation requirements are quite large.

Another question which needs to be answered before tackling such a simulation is the solubility of each polymer in the other; we discuss this in the next section. If there is a free energy gradient opposing such intersolubility, the process must be even slower and less probable, and therefore less amenable to simulation.

As in the case of polymer solutions, it has appeared more promising until recently to work with simpler lattice-based models whose more schematic nature permits longer model calculations. In one such exercise aimed at simulating the polymer–polymer interface [142], the problems were clearly separated. The goal of the work was to express the interdiffusion coefficient as a product of two factors, one expressing the thermodynamics of the two entities and their interactions, and the other depending on what can be called "kinetic" factors.

In the model system of Ref. [142], a film of pure polymer A bordered on a film of pure B, with each polymer represented by beads on a lattice, so there were only three interaction parameters in the system, A-A, A-B, and B-B. Chains of length 10 and 20 were considered with three different ratios of monomer mobility. The starting model was built up in such a way that there was a slight overlap of the layers at time zero, rather than sharp step-function concentration profiles. The profiles spread with simulation time (number of steps or lattice moves) so that the mixing region broadened. The interdiffusion rate was inversely proportional to the total concentration of material, or the fraction of lattice sites occupied. As expected on intuitive grounds, high occupancy makes all moves less likely, and the limiting case of 100% occupancy corresponds to a frozen polymer glass or crystal in which no motion is possible. If the self-diffusion rates of the two species are different, then the mixing profile will be asymmetric; in effect, the more mobile or volatile species diffuses into the free space within the interior of the other species, and the boundary layer shifts in the direction of the faster diffusion. These effects were observed in the simulations.

This schematic non-atomistic model provides a convenient way of simulating interfacial diffusion subject to several easily variable model parameters which can be interpreted in terms of material characteristics. While the results are principally qualitative rather than mechanistic, they are suggestive of many approaches that could be carried out with detailed atomistic simulations.

Kremer and Grest [143] carried out the first ambitious, large-scale computation of a simulated polymer melt, with the goal of understanding entanglement and reptation of chains. They built amorphous systems ranging in size from 50 chains of 5 monomers (extended atoms) each to 100 chains of 200 units. The total of 20,000 particles in the latter system represents a significant computational task for any meaningful length of simulation. One additional system of ten 400-unit chains was also treated. The work considered motions of both individual monomers and the chains as a whole; here we are interested primarily in the latter. The self-diffusion coefficients decreased rapidly when the chains exceeded approximately 35 units in length. This was a confirmation that the simulation had spanned the crossover region from simple Rouse dynamics to reptation. To visualize reptation, it was necessary to average out monomer motions along the chains by considering a so-called primitive chain. In this construct, each position represents the average of N_e adjacent units; a chain of N monomers thus is reduced to a primitive chain of $N + 1 - N_e$ units. For chains of length $N = 75$, traces of the motion of the primitive chain appear quite random, with no obvious confinement to a channel, but for $N = 200$ the reptation motion is visually obvious, and it is even more so for $N = 400$.

The two models discussed here, lattice Monte Carlo and molecular dynamics, form the major simulation approaches available for studying complex phenomena in melts and glasses. As applied in the examples reviewed, both are largely schematic in that they use highly uniform, modeled entities such as lattice particles and extended atoms. Among the coming challenges of computational polymer science will be simulations containing more explicit expressions of the characteristics of different polymer architectures and configurations.

7.3.4   Solubility

As mentioned above, it is attractive to try to obtain improved properties over a greater range of conditions by blending or mixing polymers. One approach to this goal can be attempted by copolymerization, which certainly is capable of modifying the properties of a starting polymer. But what is intended here is the blending of two different polymers in a mechanical sense, where the two are chosen for their complementary properties; e.g., a brittle, strong polymer would be mixed with a ductile, plastic material to try to develop a composite that is both ductile and strong. The ability to mix materials depends on the thermodynamics of mixing; a necessary condition for solution is that the free energy of mixing is negative. It is also necessary for the free energy-composition curve to be concave downward at all mixture compositions. Here we will consider the free energy component.

The change in free energy ΔG for a process is defined in terms of the change in enthalpy ΔH and the change in entropy ΔS by the relation $\Delta G = \Delta H - T \cdot \Delta S$ where T is the temperature. The entropy of mixing is positive, corresponding to a disordering of the system. Thus if the enthalpy of mixing is not too large, the free energy change will favor mixing. Hildebrand suggested that the enthalpy of mixing was related to a solubility parameter (now called the Hildebrand solubility parameter) δ. In particular, the enthalpy of mixing two species denoted 1 and 2 is [144]

$$\Delta H_{12} = v_1 v_2 (\delta_1 - \delta_2)^2$$

where v_i is the volume fraction of species i. The necessary condition for miscibility can thus be calculated from the cohesive energy densities of the components; these can be calculated, as in several of the examples of Chapters 4 and 5, as the difference between the energy of a polymeric system and the energy of its isolated chains. Alternatively, it can be viewed as the interchain portion of the nonbonded energy, where each contribution comes from the interaction of atom i in chain A and atom j in another chain $B \neq A$. The cohesive energy densities of a pair of substances can be used in various theories to predict phase equilibria.

Another approach to solubility is the Flory-Huggins theory for the free energy of mixing in a binary system [145]. The free energy of mixing is expressed in terms of volume fractions of the components and an interaction term, as follows:

$$\Delta G = RT[(\varphi_1/x_1) \ln \varphi_1 + (\varphi_2/x_2) \ln \varphi_2 + \chi \varphi_1 \varphi_2]$$

where φ is the volume fraction, x is the chain length, and χ expresses the interaction energy of the two units being mixed,

$$\chi = z \Delta w_{12}/RT$$

Here z is the effective coordination number and Δw_{12} is the energy of formation of an unlike pair, defined as

$$\Delta w_{12} = w_{12} - (w_{11} + w_{22})/2$$

Thus the free energy of mixing, and the phase behavior over the complete range of concentrations, can be estimated by calculating the interaction energies of three pairs, the two homogeneous and the one heterogeneous combination of the two components, and estimating the effective coordination number.

The application of molecular-level simulation methods to this formulation has recently been carried out by Fan *et al.* [146]. In their approach the interaction energy of a pair is obtained by sampling over all possible orientations and averaging the interaction energy. They consider three possibilities for the energy calculation in the sampling procedure: for each orientation generated for the pair of molecules, the energy may be optimized by molecular mechanics; it may be weighted by a Boltzmann factor; or a Monte Carlo acceptance criterion can be applied. In the first method all configurations are accepted and averaged; the effects of temperature are removed by the energy minimization, and this method does not correspond to sampling a Boltzmann distribution. The Monte Carlo method was chosen for this work, and the statistical error in the interaction energy was made small by generating some 100,000 pair configurations.

The effective coordination number, z, is not well defined except in strict lattice simulations where the relative positions of the components are fixed. In this work z was estimated from packing considerations, resulting in a figure somewhat below 7 for two solvent molecules, and about 5 for two polymer molecules. The resulting expression for the free energy of mixing contains explicit temperature dependence because of the sampling method used, and provides a set of isotherms for ΔG as a function of concentration. The methodology was applied to solvent–solvent, solvent–polymer, and polymer–polymer systems. The critical temperatures for solutions of polyisobutylene (at three molecular weights) in diisobutyl ketone agreed quite well with experimental data when $z = 6.5$ was used for the coordination number. Similar success was obtained for mixtures of polyisopropylene and polystyrene; the results for $z = 4$ were somewhat better than those for $z = 5$.

7.4   Energy Transfer in Polymers

As a final topic of the dynamic aspects of polymer structure, we consider energy transfer. This is the process by which external effects, whether caused by mechanical impacts, chemical reactions, or other events, are absorbed and transferred to the interior of the material. Two applications which have been studied by simulation are the impact of energetic particles on a polymer surface, and burning. In both cases the eventual participation of extents of the material remote from the initial events is important in dispersing the localized impact.

A study of particle impact [147] modeled the perpendicular collision of nitrogen molecules onto the end of a model polyethylene crystal. There are a number of possible elaborations of this calculation: non-perpendicular impacts, particles of different energy, the growth behavior of the deposited particles, etc. A potential application is to evaluate the effects of ionizing radiation on plastics and materials; formulae have been developed for the rate of deposition of energy of a beam of particles of various kinds of radiation. How the material then distributes that energy would be an important consideration in designing shields against radiation or heat.

In the model system, seven polyethylene chains which were free to undergo unconstrained molecular dynamics were surrounded by 12 static chains; these can be thought of as a solid mount or a boundary layer stabilizing the moving chains. Each chain was 100 extended atoms long and entirely in the *trans* configuration. The system thus began as a perfect crystal, with the central mobile chain surrounded by six more mobile chains, and these surrounded in hexagonal close packing arrangement by the 12 static chains. The particle impact took place directly on the end of the central moving chain. The collision behavior varied from rebounding of the impinging particle to burial up to 10 Å within the crystal. In most cases, most of the particle's energy was transferred to the crystal. The kinetic energy of atoms in the impacted chain rose to its peak within a few tenths of a picosecond after impact, then returned to an energy that was constant, but higher than before impact (i.e., there was a permanent increase in temperature). The other chains absorbed some of the energy within a few picoseconds, but also settled back to a steady state; the energy transfer was never complete. The material would become hotter as more particles struck it, unless the calculation included a stochastic mechanism for energy dissipation. The model used here was quite idealized, and not directly comparable to an experimental system, but was appropriate for the study of fundamental energy dissipation mechanisms.

A calculation that was designed to model a real system more explicitly was the combustion simulation of Nyden *et al.* [148]. The authors sought a realistic, mechanistic interpretation of burning in order to design materials that would rapidly form a burn-resistant char; cross-linked materials are known to be better for this purpose.

Since bonds must break in the burning simulation, the bond-stretching potential was represented by a Morse function; unlike the harmonic form $k(r - r_0)^2$, the Morse function permits bond breaking when an amount of energy equal to the bond dissociation energy accumulates in a bond. Indeed, in simulations at temperatures ranging from 500 to 5000 K, bond breaking occurred within the first picosecond. The other terms in the energy function were preceded by a switching function to weaken and eventually suppress them if any of the bonds involved in the internal coordinate broke. Additional provisions were made to permit formation of new bonds as a result of processes such as radical recombination.

The initial configuration of the model was either a single chain or a crystal of 13 chains, each chain having 50 carbons and 100 hydrogens in a planar zig-zag (all-*trans*) conformation. In addition to rapid bond-breaking, coiling of the sample into an amorphous ball took place a short time into the simulations. Competing effects influencing cross-link formation were seen: while the high temperature increased the mobility of polymer segments, the entangled mass sometimes prevented nearby radical pairs from moving close enough together to undergo recombination. Over the course of the simulation, cross-linking increased to produce a high molecular weight thermally stable char.

The coiling behavior of burning polymer residues was also observed in a simulation using a simpler material model [149]. Single all-*trans* chains of 50 to 950 units were built in free space and heated to a temperature equivalent to 2500 K. Again bonds broke rapidly, as fluctuations produced concentrations of energy leading to extreme extensions of random bonds. The fragments rapidly coiled, while continuing to depolymerize. Larger fragments, however, cooled rapidly, inhibiting the depolymerization events and leading to cold stable masses.

7.5   Summary

At the root of all properties and dynamic phenomena of polymers are the micromechanical processes which contribute to fluctuation and alteration of the configurational state of the material. By considering model systems and studying individual phenomena such as those reviewed in this chapter, much can be learned through a simulation approach.

Gas permeability is one of the most readily observable and measurable phenomena, and at least in concept, it is straightforward to simulate. As we have seen, the quality of results obtainable from atomistic simulations has improved considerably in just the recent few years. This aspect of polymer behavior is approaching a sufficient state of maturity to warrant regular applications in industrial research. Areas where progress remains to be made include the treatment of complicated polymers, especially blends, and the development of better methods to deal with penetrants larger than simple gases.

The study of gases in polymers leads naturally to investigations of adsorption and solubility. The nature of the polymer surface is a topic of interest, as are the phenomena that occur at surfaces. The most complicated situation is the interface between two layers of different polymers, which may form a physical bond through interdiffusion. Two types of treatments have been reviewed: highly idealized lattice simulations and more realistic atomistic simulations using molecular dynamics. Both give useful information about the types of behavior which can occur at the interface.

As an introduction to fundamental questions of internal energy transfer, the Chapter closed with two simulations, one modeling the impact of energetic particles, and the other modeling combustion. Clearly these simulations are in a more schematic and less complete state, but they give good examples of how simulation approaches may be applied to such problems.

8
Electrical Properties of Polymers

In this Chapter we explore certain aspects of the interaction of polymeric materials with electromagnetic fields and radiation. While some of the phenomenology is directly dependent on the electronic structure of the polymer chains, other behavior has to do with conformations and motional processes similar to those which govern the structural, mechanical, and diffusional properties of polymers. Before going into details and suggesting how simulations can be done, we first review the relevant phenomena [150].

Considering first the electronic description, we can make the fundamental differentiation of saturated as opposed to unsaturated structures. The prototypical examples at the two extremes are polyethylene, whose fully saturated hydrocarbon structure resists the movement of electrons along the polymer chains, and polyacetylene, whose extensive π-orbital system is much better suited to permit such movement. Many other polymers, containing various types and amounts of conjugated and aromatic moieties, may also show increased electronic conduction. A simple example is poly(paraphenylene), Fig. 8.1, whose aromatic groups provide delocalized electrons for conduction. This example also makes clearer the interaction of conformation with electronic structure; if the polymer chains are so arranged as to dispose all the phenylene groups in coplanarity, the opportunities for conduction will be much greater than in a coiled chain where adjacent phenylene groups bear no particular spatial relationship to each other. Below we review several case studies in which such effects are calculated.

Conduction can be also be the consequence of ionic rather than electronic migration. The conductivity of polyacetylene can be increased to that of copper by sufficient doping with ionic species. Amorphous polymers are also of interest for ionic conductivity, since they may present advantages in fabrication and processing, yet with proper doping can still supply adequate ionic conductivity. For this to occur there must be sufficient ionic binding sites, arranged to permit convenient hopping from one to the next, for the polymer to be useful as a conductor. The hopping phenomenon is reminiscent of the mechanisms of gas diffusion studied in the previous chapter, even though the interaction of an ionic species with the polymer matrix may well be different from that of a neutral gas molecule, and the molecular motions and relaxations at work there must also be important in ionic conductivity.

Traditionally, polymeric materials were more likely to be viewed as insulators and dielectrics, along the lines of polyethylene. Of course there may be relatively low but non-zero conductivity values even for these dielectric materials. The phenomena of interest have to do with how the materials interact with fields and radiation. When placed in a constant field, the material may be capable of resisting or opposing the field through motions or structural adjustments that orient the internal dipoles in opposition to the field. If the field is strong enough, dielectric breakdown occurs and the material can no longer resist. If the field begins to alternate, motional processes in the polymer can adjust rapidly enough to oppose the field throughout its cycle; as the frequency of alternation rises, these processes can keep pace over a range of frequencies, but at some critical frequency it is no longer possible for molecular motions to occur sufficiently fast. The dielectric constant of the material drops to a new, lower level. The change is not a step-function, instead occurring over a range of frequencies, because different environments in the polymer have greater or lesser mobility, permitting the dipoles to reorient at slightly different maximum rates. Over the transition range, the material also exhibits a complex dielectric component, associated with absorption of electromagnetic energy, which peaks at the critical frequency and then subsides at higher frequencies. The critical frequency at which the transition occurs clearly depends on the chemical composition and molecular architecture of the polymeric substance.

There are many additional phenomena of a more complex nature. One area of great interest in current materials science is non-linear optics [151]. For most materials and for moderate external fields, the electrical response within the material depends linearly on the field strength. At field values dependent on the nature of the material, non-linear effects become measurable. The ordinary or linear polarizability of a material can be viewed at the molecular level in terms of electron shifts resulting from the imposed field. In molecules with electron donating or accepting groups, the electrons will shift differently, and these additional positive or negative contributions will alter the polarizability. Such nonlinear effects are characterized as hyper-polarizabilities. The creation of nonlinear materials involves placing the nonlinear chromophores into the material in an oriented or regular fashion. Approaches include doping and copolymerization; in the latter case, the chromophore may be incorporated as a main-chain group or a side group. The computation of nonlinear properties of chromophores involves electronic calculations. Some aspects of the evaluation of the nonlinear character of a material sample may be approached with conformational energy calculations that indicate how oriented the material is under various conditions of temperature and mechanical stress. We will not cover nonlinear phenomena of polymers further in this book.

These simple qualitative descriptions suggest how calculations of electronic structure, conformational energies, chain structures, and internal dynamics can be useful in understanding the electromagnetic properties of polymers. Through further descriptions and examples, we will now discuss some applications of these calculation methods. Section 8.1 introduces electronic calculations on polymers, whereas Section

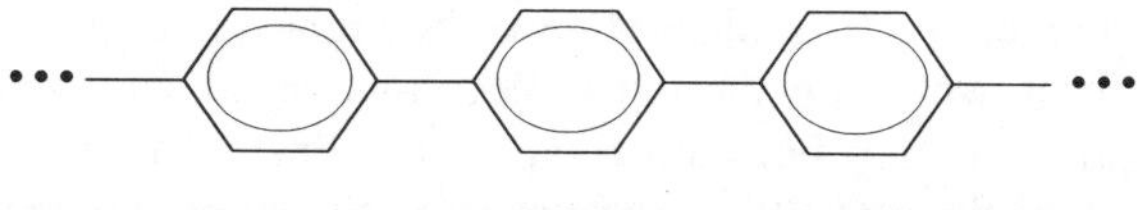

Figure 8.1. The conjugated aromatic structure of poly(paraphenylene) provides delocalized electrons for conduction.

8.2 considers the interplay between electronic and conformational factors for polyaromatics and lattices. Section 8.3 shows a simple example of how UV/visible spectroscopic phenomena can be accounted for by modeling calculations. The molecular dynamics modeling of dielectric properties forms Section 8.4.

8.1   Electronic Calculations in Extended Systems

This book has been written to emphasize the application to polymer phenomena of force-field calculations of the conformational energy. In Chapters 1 and 2 there were brief mentions of electronic structure calculations, and how these lead to force fields under the assumption or approximation that electronic structure adjusts essentially instantaneously to changes in the nuclear coordinates. Thus force fields model the time-averaged potential energy set up by the electronic state, and make possible a classical mechanical description of static deformations and dynamic behavior of molecules. As outlined above, in the study of electrical properties of polymers, there are significant effects due to the interplay of conformation and electronic states, and force field calculations are of considerable value.

However, some aspects of the phenomenon of electronic conduction cannot be approached without considering the electrons explicitly. In isolated molecules, the concepts of molecular orbitals and their associated energy levels are familiar to all chemists, even though the computational methods may not be. There are bonding and anti-bonding orbitals lying at different discrete energy levels, and in the ground state, the lowest half of these are populated by electrons. As the molecule becomes larger, as in going from the monomer to the dimer to the trimer, and so on, there are more energy levels, and the spacings become smaller. Because electronic calculations require significant computational resources, the direct evaluation of the energy levels can be carried out only for small oligomers; it is necessary to use some sort of periodic boundary condition to extrapolate the results to an infinite polymer chain or other extended systems. It is not the intention of this book to present this methodology. Instead, the reader is referred to texts on solid-state physics [152], and especially to a review article [153] which attempts to explain the concepts of solid-state physics in chemical terms.

The essential outcome of such electronic calculations is to determine the character of a polymer chain along the continuum ranging from saturation and electrical insulation at one end, to unsaturation and semiconduction at the other. One measure of this character is the electronic band gap, or the energy required to promote electrons from localized or valence states, to delocalized or conducting states. For isolated molecules used as models of polymeric systems, this can be approximated by the distance, on an energetic scale, between the highest occupied molecular orbital, or HOMO, and the lowest unoccupied molecular orbital, or LUMO. The energies of these orbitals, and the gap between them, may vary with changes in the internal geometry of the molecule, and this is the basis for the significance of conformational calculations in contributing to an understanding of conduction possibilities.

8.2   Electronic Properties and Molecular Structure

In this section we review several examples in which the connection between geometry and electronic structure has been studied for polymeric systems of commercial interest. Most of these materials are considered as "tunable" electronic systems, whose specific conduction properties can be varied to some extent by the amount and type of ionic doping materials added. Calculations of the pure polymer, however, are used to determine the suitability of the material as an electronic medium. The calculations can be confined to the study of individual groups along the polymer chain, or can encompass the interaction of chain structure with crystal unit cell parameters.

8.2.1   Planarity and Conjugation in Aromatic Subunits

The first case concerns sulfur-containing aromatic monomers, two of which are sketched in Fig. 8.2. The planar units, when joined in oligomers or polymers, are connected to a common bond, and the possibility of steric hindrance is apparent for transoid and especially for cisoid structures (here *trans* and *cis* refer to the disposition of the sulfurs about the monomer-joining bond). Discussing the structures and electronic properties, Nayak and Marynick [154] noted that previous calculations assumed planar structures and attempted no geometry optimization. One earlier calculation suggested that electronic delocalization was sufficient to overcome steric repulsions. The calculations considered here employed an approximate molecular orbital method which has been successful in predicting structures of partially aromatic compounds, and which is thus appropriate to answer questions about the geometry of the dimers of the structures shown in Fig. 8.2. There are also different resonance forms that must be considered with these dimers: in one, the aromatic form, the connecting bond has only partial double-bond character; in the alternative quinoid form, it is explicitly a double-bond. Calculations on the aromatic form showed definite

(a)   (b)

Figure 8.2. (a) Isothianaphthalene (ITN). (b) Isonaphthothiophene (INT).

steric hindrance in the transoid form between each sulfur atom and the hydrogen of the six-membered ring of the other monomer. This steric hindrance amounted to approximately 15 kcal/mol in a planar cisoid geometry but was reduced by rotating about the joining bond; the angle between monomer planes in the geometry-optimized dimer is about 120°. The same phenomenon operates in both of the structures shown in Fig. 8.2. Additional calculations to substantiate these results are described in the original paper, Ref. [154].

From these conformational calculations it is possible to design other monomers in which the sources of steric hindrance are reduced or removed. Such structures have no difficulty forming planar oligomers and polymers that should show improved conduction possibilities. Two compounds considered in Ref. [154] were calculated to have significantly lower band gaps, and should be very interesting electronic materials. Thus this work not only demonstrates the subtle interplay between geometric and electronic structures, but also shows how the information derived can be used in structure-based design for properties of interest.

The same research group performed similar calculations [155] on polymers containing alternating substituted phenylene and bithiophene groups (see Fig. 8.3). Again, the co-planarity of the phenyl ring with the thiophene ring depends on a balance of electronic and steric factors, and is likely to be significantly influenced by the phenyl substituents. The most straightforward comparison is between the unsubstituted structure ($R_1 = R_2 = H$) and a dimethyl monomer ($R_1 = R_2 = CH_3$). The approximate molecular orbital calculations on the unsubstituted monomer yielded an inter-ring dihedral angle of about 24° and a relatively low barrier to internal rotation of about 3.1 kcal/mol. By comparison, the dimethyl monomer had a dihedral angle of 63° and a rotation barrier of almost 16 kcal/mol. As expected, this causes the dimethyl compound to have much lower conductivity. Structural verification was obtained by several spectral and thermal methods, and direct measurements of the electrical properties completed the work.

Two further applications of structure calculation to explanations of electronic properties of polyaromatics are also mentioned here because they concern different chemical units. Polyimides, studied by Kafafi *et al.* [156], are of interest in the electronics industries because of their good thermal and structural properties and the wide range of behavior obtainable with different dopants. In addition, the ability to etch fine patterns onto polyimide surfaces with UV radiation renders them of value in microelectronics and electronic packaging. Polyanaline, studied by Ginder

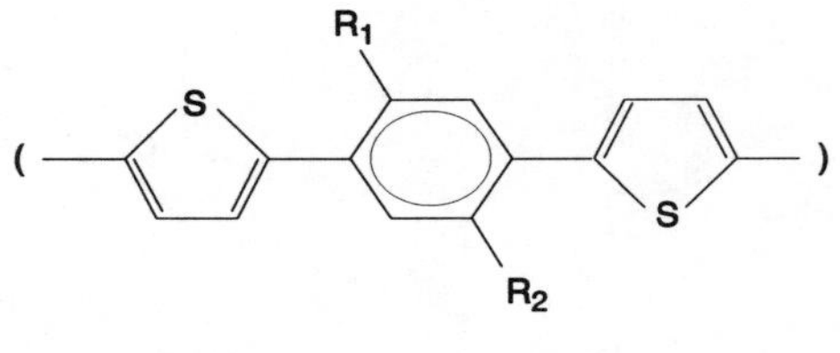

Figure 8.3. Substituted 1,4-di-2-thienylbenzenes.

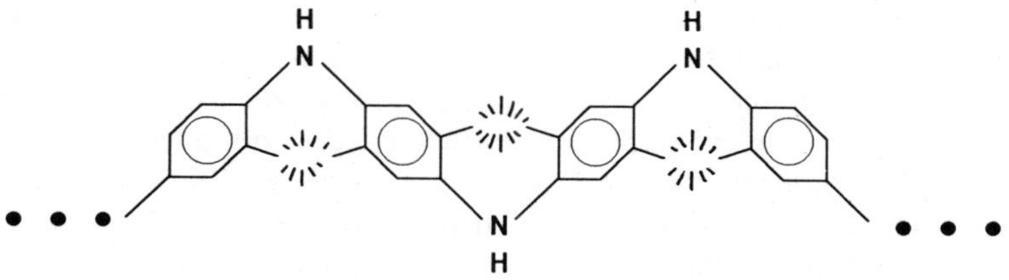

Figure 8.4. Polyaniline as the fully reduced leucoemeraldine base; the phenyl hydrogens would cause appreciable steric repulsions in the planar form.

and Epstein [157], is an interesting case of a polymer whose aromatic structure is interrupted by the heteroatom nitrogen between each phenyl group.

Both semiempirical quantum-mechanical methods and empirical force field calculations were employed in the first of these two studies to evaluate the planarity of the representative polyimide model compound. Both methods found the angle between the phenyl and the imide planes to be about 30°, with this torsion producing an energy savings of about 2 kcal/mol over the planar structure. This behavior was explained using a qualitative argument based on sketches of the 16 highest occupied and eight lowest unoccupied molecular orbitals. The energy gap, electron affinity, and ionization potential were computed, and an estimate of the interchain electron hopping barrier was made.

Polyanaline exists in several oxidation states, but in the fully reduced leucoemeraldine base form, Fig. 8.4, the phenyl hydrogens would engender substantial steric hindrance in a planar structure. This fully reduced base is studied in the calculations of Ginder and Epstein. A potential for phenylene rotation is mapped out; its minimum occurs at 56° from planarity, with an asymmetric profile giving a lower barrier to rotation through 90° of about 3.3 kcal/mol and a larger barrier through planarity of about 16 kcal/mol.

This explicit calculation of the potential well for ring torsion points out the possibilities for interactions of ring dynamics with electronic phenomena. The potential is broad enough to permit ring torsional oscillations of considerable amplitude at room temperature, and these would become larger with increasing temperature. A number of experimentally accessible effects, involving relaxation phenomena and various kinds of dispersion arising from the distribution of ring environments, are likely to be associated with these motions. Finally, the interaction between individual polyanaline chains would be expected to modify these results, both through direct effects on the band-gap calculation and indirectly by changing the torsional potentials. Such multi-chain calculations, however, even with semiempirical methods, would involve much greater levels of computational effort.

8.2.2   Optimization of Lattices as Well as Internal Geometries

Calculations involving monomers, oligomers, and even semi-infinite chains ignore the interactions between different chains. In amorphous polymers these are irregular but significant; in crystalline polymers, they are the basis of the crystal packing and determine the lattice symmetry and dimensions. In this section we review a simulation of the lattices of both pure [158] and doped [159] polyacetylene and polypara-phenylene, two prototypical and well-characterized conjugated polymers. X-ray, neutron-, and electron-diffraction work on these crystals has found general agreement on lattice parameters, but in no case was it possible to determine atomic positions. The lattices are orthorhombic or nearly so; for polyacetylene the lattice parameters are $a = 7.3$ to 7.4, $b = 4.1$ to 4.2, and $c = 4.96$. The setting angle, or the inclination of the plane of the carbon skeleton to the a axis (see Fig. 8.5), varied among 24°, 51°, and 55° in three studies. The data for polyparaphenylene agree around $a = 7.8$, $b = 5.5$, and $c = 4.2$, with setting angles of 45° or 57°.

In the diffraction results, atomic positions were estimated by model-building using idealized bond lengths and bond angles. In the simulations reviewed here (Refs. [158 and 159]), geometric flexibility was taken into account by using a Morse potential for bonds, a harmonic valence angle bending potential, and potentials of the exponential-6 form for the three types of nonbonded interactions, $H\cdots H$, $C\cdots H$, and $C\cdots C$. The structures were required to remain planar, with no torsional flexibility permitted (but the C—C bondlengths and the C—C—C valence angles were allowed to vary in the minimization). Energy minimizations were started from the experimental geometries. Those with the larger setting angle minimized to a final crystal structure with a setting angle of 62°, while the structure with initial setting angle 24° minimized to 22°. In repeated trials it was found that 35° was the approximate dividing point; structures started with setting angles greater than 35° minimized to the first minimum, while those started at lower angles went to the second. When the energy was calculated as a function of setting angle for *rigid* polymer chains started in one of the unit cell forms, a potential with only one

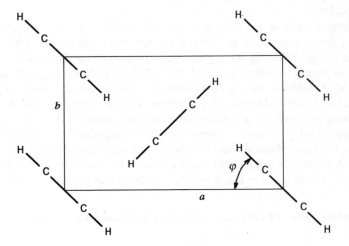

Figure 8.5. Definition of the setting angle φ in the polyacetylene crystal.

minimum, at 51°, results. Thus the finding of two polymorphs is dependent on the use of flexible chain geometry.

Minimizations of an all-planar polyparaphenylene produced three polymorphs; two had similar orthorhombic lattices, with setting angles of 62° for the more stable one and 39° for the other. Another local minimum involved somewhat more change in the lattice parameters, resulting in a tetragonal lattice ($a = b$) and a setting angle of 45°. A map of the energy of rigid chains as a function of setting angle shows a minimum at about 60° and a very shallow, broad well at less than 20°. The two orthorhombic lattices are in reasonable agreement with experiment, but there is no evidence to support the tetragonal structure.

In the earlier examples in this chapter we have seen how steric hindrance between adjacent monomers was balanced against electronic factors which favor perfect planarity. In Ref. [158] the authors noted experimental evidence from smaller phenylenes and oligophenylenes of such alternating out-of-plane twisting and carried out an additional simulation to study this possibility. In a fixed lattice, the rings minimized to an alternating conformation with about 30° between adjacent pairs (i.e., each ring 15° above or below the average ring plane); if the lattice was permitted to vary, two conformations resulted, one fully planar and the other with 71° between adjacent rings. The latter value is large compared to what is seen in oligophenylenes, but it is noted that the potentials used in this study do not take account of π-electron effects that would favor ring stacking as a means of stabilizing the lattice.

In the companion paper, the same research group then extended the simulations to include dopants, which were introduced at definite lattice positions but subsequently permitted to move during the energy minimization [159]. These dopants, which carry electric charge and may have internal structure, must be added to the simulation models. Lithium and potassium ions interacted with each other and with the hydrocarbon lattice through both nonbonded and electrostatic potentials. The neutral arsenic pentafluoride, AsF_5, involves internal degrees of freedom (the As—F stretch and the F—As—F bend). Nonbonded potentials were calculated for the fluorines only; any effects due to the central arsenic atom were assumed to be taken care of by a proper choice of the fluorine radii. For the negatively charged AsF_6^-, each fluorine atom was assigned a charge of $-1/6$ electron. For charged dopants, mechanisms were worked out to distribute excess charge over the hydrocarbon atoms. Thus the previous simulations were augmented and complicated by the additional potentials and the additional degrees of freedom associated with the dopant species.

To begin the simulations, experimental data were reviewed and used to construct models with appropriate internal geometries and ion placements. The data show that potassium-doped polyacetylene has uniform C—C bondlengths, instead of the alternating lengths in the pristine (undoped) polymer. The structure investigated has square channels in which ions occupy sites along the channels formed by offset polymer chains, as in Fig. 8.6. Another somewhat different structure was not modeled. Two doping levels were considered, one with one potassium ion for every eight CH centers, and one with twice as much potassium.

Initial minimizations produced a structure with significantly altered lattice dimensions, which prompted the investigators to revise the ion-polymer nonbonded

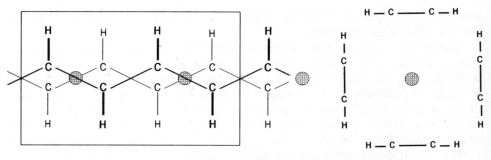

Figure 8.6. Orthogonal views of model structure of K⁺-doped polyacetylene crystal.

potentials. This led to satisfactory minimizations in which the final structures resembled the experimental ones, and in which the ions remained in their original sites over the centers of the C—C bonds. These structures were stable under distortion and displacement of the ions.

Similar calculations of lithium- and potassium-doped polyparaphenylene represent straightforward applications of the same techniques. With calculations of this type, one can readily study the effects of dopant concentration, starting lattice characteristics, and assumptions about flexibility of the polymer chain.

The calculations with AsF_5 and AsF_6^- as dopants were more complicated, due to the existence of internal degrees of freedom in the dopants and their larger sizes, which increase their interactions with the polymer lattice. Another aspect of the molecular model to be decided was how charge is transferred between the species. As mentioned above, in AsF_6^- each fluorine atom was assigned $-1/6$ electron, but various hydrocarbon charge assignments were tried. A number of initial attempts, at various doping levels and occupancy sites, produced unstable lattices that would not minimize to satisfactory dimensions, if at all. The conclusion of the work, however, is that force-field molecular modeling of doped polymers is a valid and usable means of investigating the structures of these systems. Similar applications to systems in which the conductivity is due to defects, not ions, are also envisioned.

8.3   Spectroscopy of Polymers

We have referred earlier to the use of spectroscopy in various ranges of the electromagnetic spectrum to probe internal structure and motion of polymers. For example, spectra in the infrared and Raman range give information about restoring forces associated with internal coordinates, and can be used as measures of the intermolecular interactions which slightly perturb characteristic frequencies. NMR spectra arise from motions of magnetic moments carried by protons and other nuclei, and yield information about motions which, though relatively slower than molecular vibrations, can be simulated by molecular dynamics.

A variety of spectral techniques reveal information about the electronic structures of polymers and are thus relevant to the material of this chapter. Among the methods are ultraviolet and X-ray photoelectron spectroscopy (UPS and XPS, respectively), electron spectroscopy for chemical analysis (ESCA), fluorescence spectroscopy, secondary electron emission (SEE), electron energy loss spectroscopy (EELS), and others. They have in common the ability to probe the electronic transitions which measure or are associated with the gap between valence and conducting states. Data from one or more of these spectroscopic methods is used to verify or compare with calculated results in most of the case studies covered in this chapter.

One illustrative example of how structure calculations can be correlated with spectroscopic experiments is the characterization of an intramolecular excimer in poly(p-*tert*-butylstyrene) [160]. An excimer occurs when an electronic excitation is able to resonate between chemically identical chromophores; in this case, the excitation is the singlet excited state of a phenyl or substituted phenyl group in polystyrene. Resonance requires a coplanar arrangement of two rings, at a distance between ring planes of about 3 to 4 Å. The excimer is observed by fluorescence spectroscopy as a broad peak in the ultraviolet spectral range; for polystyrene, it occurs at 335 nm. It does not shift appreciably when each phenyl group contains a *para*-methyl substituent, but it moves to 323 nm (a shorter wavelength and therefore higher energy) if the substituent is the bulky *tert*-butyl group.

Straightforward molecular modeling of diads, or dimers, of polystyrene and the *tert*-butyl substituted polystyrene rationalize the fluorescence peak shift. In most main-chain orientations, the rings are too far apart to form an excimer. In the all-*trans* (or *tt*) dimer, the distances are satisfactory, and the rings are nearly ideally stacked. Minimization of the unsubstituted dimer causes the rings to bow outward very slightly from each other, but they remain within 6° of coplanarity. The bulky substituent, on the other hand, causes the rings to be pushed away from each other to relieve the steric hindrance between the two substituent groups. The ring planes differ by about 22°, while remaining reasonably centered with respect to each other. This is consistent with continued excimer formation, but at a wavelength shifted toward higher energy.

8.4   Dielectric Relaxation Dynamics

The characteristic important in non-conducting applications of polymers is the insulating quality of the material (effectively, its dielectric constant). The dielectric constant is the factor by which charges are "diluted" when they interact with each other through the dielectric material. Coulomb's law in vacuum gives the interaction energy of two charges q_i and q_j separated by a distance r_{ij} as

$$E = q_i \cdot q_j / r_{ij}$$

In the presence of dielectric material this is modified to:

$$E = q_i \cdot q_j / D \cdot r_{ij}$$

where D is the dielectric constant, considered to be a continuous macroscopic property of the material. The mechanism by which materials thus "resist" an external field can be thought of as the orientation of electron distributions in opposition to the field. In a simple model, the electron cloud, otherwise spherical, distorts because of the field (Fig. 8.7).

If the field is not static but oscillatory, as in the case of electromagnetic radiation, the induced dipoles can reorient so as to cancel the field. If this reorientation involves motions of small groups in a highly mobile material matrix, the reorientation may be able to "keep up" with the field up to high frequencies. At some high enough frequency, however, depending on the molecular groups involved and the nature of the material, the dipoles can no longer move rapidly enough to oppose the field, and the dielectric constant of the material is reduced. Since the local environment varies over the material, the transition occurs over a range of frequencies. Temperature also has an effect, as it makes groups more mobile. In this respect there is a connection with mechanical phenomena, where the motions are induced by mechanical stresses rather than imposed fields. A cold, glassy material whose internal motions are restricted would not be able to keep up with a mechanical stress cycle, just as its dipoles could not reorient rapidly in response to an oscillating field.

Molecular dynamics provides a method for the simulation of dipole reorientations. The motions involved may be localized and rapid, as in a normal mode vibration, or delocalized and slower, as in segmental motions of polymer chains. The latter type of loose, floppy motion would be observed in the far infrared range, in the range of 30 to 3 cm^{-1}. The latter figure corresponds to a frequency of 10^{11} Hz, i.e., a period of 10^{-11} sec, or 10 picoseconds, well within the range of molecular dynamics simulations that we have discussed earlier in this book.

Molecular dynamics trajectories can be analyzed by calculating the instantaneous dipole moments of molecules or groups at different times during the trajectory. The oscillation of such moments is likely to be rapid and difficult to characterize in a

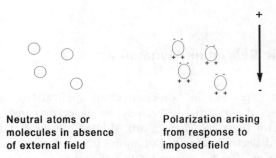

Neutral atoms or
molecules in absence
of external field

Polarization arising
from response to
imposed field

Figure 8.7. Electronic origin of polarization in a dielectric material. *Left:* neutral atoms or molecules in absence of external field. *Right:* polarization arising from response to imposed field.

systematic way. More useful is the autocorrelation function, which expresses the probability of finding a dipole moment in the same alignment as earlier, as a function of time elapsed between the two points compared. For a free dipole undergoing random thermal motions, the memory of its initial alignment is uniformly lost as time passes. For a dipole constrained within a polymer network, the behavior is likely to be quite different as the dipole is constrained against varying far from its original orientation, and is governed more by regular periodic motions.

A molecular dynamics study based on these methods has been reported by Tiller [161]. Its objective was the identification and characterization of relaxation motions in the microwave frequency range (10^8–10^{11} Hz) for applications to microwave cookware, and to "stealth" materials that reduce radar signatures, among others. This frequency range corresponds to periods of 10 psec to 10 nsec; 10 psec is well within the range of polymer dynamics simulations, while 10 nsec represents a major computation if the polymer model is at all larger than a small, schematic one. In this work, the systems simulated were: isolated polystyrene chains of 25 repeat units (simulated for 10 psec with various stereochemistries); an amorphous polystyrene cell (5 psec); and a polyimide of two sizes (197 atoms and 392 atoms) and configurations (helical and zigzag) simulated for 5 psec or less.

An example of the motion of the dipole moment of a single isolated polystyrene chain is shown in Figs. 8.8a and b. Part a shows the rapid variation of the magnitude of the chain's dipole vector over a 3-psec simulation period, while Fig. 8.8b shows the dipole autocorrelation function. Though the overall magnitude of the autocorrelation vector slowly declines (memory of the initial orientation is slowly lost) the short-term oscillations, at about 20 periods per psec or 2×10^{13} Hz, stand out clearly. A more precise interpretation of the autocorrelation function is obtained by Fourier transforming it so that it is stated in terms of the frequency components involved. The dominant 2×10^{13} Hz feature then stands out as a strong band at

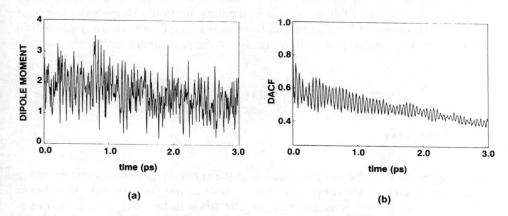

Figure 8.8. (a) Variation of the dipole moment for an isolated polystyrene chain. (b) Autocorrelation function for the dipole variations in (a). Reprinted with permission from Ref. 161. Copyright 1992 American Chemical Society.

650 cm^{-1}. Considerable structure occurs around that frequency, and also at frequencies below approximately 200 cm^{-1}.

The motions associated with these dipole oscillations are identified by, in essence, filtering out all motions except those within a frequency window about 10 cm^{-1} in width. The filtered motion is observed on a graphics workstation, or it can be characterized analytically in terms of internal coordinate distortions. The slower motions of interest in this work were described as backbone C—C rotations (similar to the crankshaft motions discussed in Chapter 5, Sec. 5.5) in the range below 20 cm^{-1}; and a variety of individual and correlated phenyl group ring rotations in the range from 35 to 100 cm^{-1}. The more rapid (650 cm^{-1}) components are identified with internal phenyl group breathing motions, which are quite independent of the polymer's tacticity and conformation. The latter frequency is also observed in small molecules with simply substituted phenyl groups.

Similar treatment of the four polyimide single-chain models produced trajectories whose dominant frequency component occurred at 110 cm^{-1}, with additional features in the neighborhood of 20 cm^{-1} and below. The faster motions are complicated oscillations within the monomer units, involving out-of-phase torsions about the nitrogen-phenyl bonds. The slower motions exhibit a different structure and intensity in the two models, with a wider distribution and more modes in the longer sample. This is a logical consequence of the fact that longer chains have more slow, diffuse modes. One of them identified for the shorter model involves bending and twisting along the entire chain; it is likened to the twisting of one end of a piece of string. The nature of such modes is compared for the zig-zag and helical configurations of both the shorter and longer polyimide models.

This paper concludes by discussing some simplified versions of molecular motions proposed earlier as mechanisms to account for dielectric relaxations. They are simplified, intuitive descriptions involving elementary motions of small structural elements, e.g., rotation of a polar group in a sidechain. Molecular dynamics, in contrast, provides a fully detailed description of intramolecular motions in all their complexity, and is not limited to such elementary motions. Despite the fact that questions remain about techniques and force field accuracy, the detailed simulation approach provides much greater illumination of the phenomena involved.

8.5   Summary

This Chapter has presented an introduction to the applications of molecular modeling methods in studies of electrical and optical phenomena. Some aspects of polymer behavior in this area depend in detail on electronic states, and require quantum-mechanical calculations of fundamental molecular properties such as electronic band structures and the parameters that characterize non-linear behavior. In other cases, the interaction between molecular conformation and electronic properties permits useful knowledge to be gained from relatively simpler conformational energy calculations. Finally, there are situations and phenomena for which simplifying assumptions such as fixed dipoles and charge distributions can be used while carrying out molecular dynamics to estimate the mobility and orientational persistence of these attributes. The simulation approach is likely to become increasingly useful as new materials are designed for future applications that place specific and simultaneous requirements on chemical, mechanical, and electrical properties.

References

1. For general descriptions of the concept of polymer design, see F. Case, J.N. Winter, and D.C. Bott, *Chemistry & Industry*, 784–786 (3 Dec 1990), Molecular modelling for designer polymers; D.C. Bott, D.M. Service, and J.N. Winter, *Chemistry in Britain* **28**, 433–436 (May 1992), Designer Polymers.
2. N.C. Cohen, J.M. Blaney, C. Humblet, P. Gund, and D.C. Barry, *J. Med. Chem.* **33**, 883–894 (1990), Molecular modeling software and methods for medicinal chemistry.
3. Walt Disney Productions, *Our Friend the Atom*, Simon and Schuster, New York (1956).
4. W.L. Koltun, *Biopolymers* **3**, 665–679 (1965), Precision space-filling atomic models.
5. D.J. Cram, *Science* **240**, 760–767 (6 May 1988), The design of molecular hosts, guests, and their complexes.
6. J.D. Watson, *The Double Helix; A Personal Account of the Discovery of the Structure of DNA*, Atheneum, New York (1968).
7. D.H. Meadows, D.L. Meadows, and J. Randers, *Beyond the Limits*, Chelsea Green Publ. Co., Post Mills, VT (1992). This is a general-audience account of the economic forecasting models first brought to widespread public attention by the "Club of Rome" report *Limits to Growth* in the 1970s.
8. P.E. Rouse, Jr., *J. Chem. Phys.* **21**, 1272–1280 (1953), A theory of the linear viscoelastic properties of dilute solutions of coiling polymers.
9. B.H. Zimm, *J. Chem. Phys.* **24**, 269–278 (1956), Dynamics of polymer molecules in dilute solution: Viscoelasticity, flow birefringence, and dielectric loss.
10. P.J. Flory, *Statistical Mechanics of Chain Molecules*, Hanser Publishers, Munich (1989).
11. See, for example, K. Kremer and K. Binder, *Comp. Phys. Reports* **7**, 259 (1988), which contains an extensive list of references on Monte Carlo technique.
12. For a more detailed introduction to the various levels of approach, see, for example, T. Clark, *A Handbook of Computational Chemistry*, John Wiley & Sons, New York (1985).
13. P.A.M. Dirac, *Proc. Roy. Soc. (London)* **123**, 714 (1929): "The underlying physical laws necessary for the mathematical theory of a large part of physics and the whole of chemistry are thus completely known, and the difficulty is only that the exact application of these laws leads to equations much too complicated to be soluble."
14. J.A. Pople and D.L. Beveridge, *Approximate Molecular Orbital Theory*, McGraw-Hill, New York (1970).
15. M.J.S. Dewar and W. Thiel, *J. Am. Chem. Soc.* **99**, 4899–4907 (1977), Ground states of molecules. 38. The MNDO method. Approximations and parameters.
16. M.J.S. Dewar, E.G. Zoebisch, E.F. Healy, and J.J.P. Stewart, *J. Am. Chem. Soc.* **107**, 3902–3909 (1985), AM1: A new general purpose quantum mechanical molecular model.
17. J.J.P. Stewart, *J. Comp. Chem.* **10**, 209–220 (1989), Optimization of parameters for semiempirical methods. I. Method.
18. J.J.P. Stewart, *J. Comp.-Aided Molec. Design* **4**, 1–105 (1990), MOPAC: A semiempirical molecular orbital program.
19. D. Bakowies and W. Thiel, *J. Am. Chem. Soc.* **113**, 3704–3714 (1991), MNDO study of large carbon clusters.
20. J.A. McCammon, B.R. Gelin, and M. Karplus, *Nature* **267**, 585–590 (1977), Dynamics of folded proteins.

21. J.A. McCammon and S.C. Harvey, *Molecular Dynamics of Proteins and Nucleic Acids*, Cambridge University Press, New York (1987).
22. M. Allen and D. Tildesley, *Computer Simulation of Liquids*, Clarendon Press, Oxford (1987).
23. C.L. Brooks III, M. Karplus, and B.M. Pettitt, *Proteins: A Theoretical Perspective of Dynamics, Structure, and Thermodynamics, Adv. in Chem. Physics*, Vol. LXXI, John Wiley & Sons, New York (1988).
24. A.E. Mark and W.F. van Gunsteren, *Biochemistry* **31**, 7745–7748 (1992), Simulation of the thermal degradation of hen egg white lysozyme: Trapping the molten globule state.
25. S. Karaborni, N.M. van Os, K. Esselink, and P.A.J. Hilbers, *Langmuir* **9**, 1175–1178 (1993), Molecular dynamics of oil solubilization in surfactant solutions.
26. A. Nakano, L. Bi, R.K. Kalia, and P. Vashishta, *Phys. Rev. Lett.* **71**, 85–88 (1993), Structural correlations in porous silica: Molecular dynamics simulations on a parallel computer.
27. E.M. Engler, J.D. Andose, and P. von R. Schleyer, *J. Am. Chem. Soc.* **95**, 8005–8025 (1973), Critical evaluation of molecular mechanics.
28. D. Hall and N. Pavitt, *J. Comp. Chem.* **5**, 441–450 (1984), An appraisal of molecular force fields for the representation of polypeptides.
29. B.R. Gelin, Testing and comparison of empirical force fields: Techniques and problems, in *Computer Simulation of Biomolecular Systems*, Vol. 2, ESCOM Science Publishers, Leiden (1993), Eds., W.F. van Gunsteren, P.K. Weiner, and A.J. Wilkinson.
30. D.B. Boyd and K.D. Lipkowitz, *Reviews in Computational Chemistry* (annual volumes), VCH Publishers (1990*ff*).
31. For a listing of commercial vendors and the programs they offer, see M.M. Ambos, B.R. Gelin, and A.B. Richon, *Computational Chemistry Yellow Pages*, Ozmeg Productions, St. Louis and Boston (1992).
32. W. Kolos and L. Wolniewicz, *J. Chem. Phys.* **41**, 3663–3673 (1964), Accurate adiabatic treatment of the ground state of the hydrogen molecule.
33. W. Kolos and L. Wolniewicz, *J. Chem. Phys.* **43**, 2429–2441 (1965), Potential-energy curves for the $X\ ^1\Sigma_u +$, $b\ ^3\Sigma_u +$, and $C\ ^1\Pi_u$ states of the hydrogen molecule.
34. W. Kolos and L. Wolniewicz, *J. Chem. Phys.* **48**, 3672–3680 (1968), Vibrational and rotational energies for the $b\ ^3\Sigma_u +$, $C\ ^1\Pi_u$, and $a\ ^3\Sigma_g +$ states of the hydrogen molecule.
35. M. Froimowitz, *BioTechniques* **8**, 640–652 (1990), The development of computer simulations of the geometries and thermodynamics of biological molecules.
36. E.B. Wilson, J.C. Decius, and P.C. Cross, *Molecular Vibrations*, McGraw-Hill, New York (1955).
37. E.L. Eliel, N.L. Allinger, S.J. Angyal, and G.A. Morrison, *Conformational Analysis*, John Wiley & Sons, New York (1965).
38. S. Lifson and A. Warshel, *J. Chem. Phys.* **49**, 5116–5129 (1968), Consistent force field for calculations of conformations, vibrational spectra, and enthalpies of cycloalkane and *n*-alkane molecules.
39. T.A. Halgren, *J. Am. Chem. Soc.* **112**, 4710–4723 (1990), Maximally diagonal force constants in dependent angle-bending coordinates. 2. Implications for the design of empirical force fields.
40. B.R. Gelin, Ph.D. thesis, Harvard University (1976), p. 165.
41. F.A. Momany, V.J. Klimkowski, and L. Schäfer, *J. Comp. Chem.* **11**, 654–662 (1990), On the use of conformationally dependent geometry trends from *ab initio* dipeptide studies to refine potentials for the empirical force field CHARMM.
42. J.R. Maple, U. Dinur, and A.T. Hagler, *Proc. Natl. Acad. Sci. USA* **85**, 5350–5354 (1988), Derivation of force fields for molecular mechanics and dynamics from *ab initio* energy surfaces.
43. S.L. Mayo, B.D. Olafson, and W.A. Goddard III, *J. Phys. Chem.* **94**, 8897–8909 (1990), DREIDING: A generic force field for molecular simulations.
44. The WIZARD program: A.R. Leach, K. Prout, and D.P. Dolata, *J. Comp.-Aided Molec. Design* **4**, 271–282 (1990), Automated conformational analysis: Algorithms for the efficient construction of low-energy conformations.
45. The CONCORD program: A. Rusinko, J.M. Skell, R. Balducci, C.M. McGarity, and R.S. Pearlman, *CONCORD*: A program for the rapid generation of high-quality approximate 3-dimensional molecular structures, Univ. of Texas at Austin, and Tripos Associates, St. Louis (1988).

46. G. Ferenczy, C.A. Reynolds, and W.G. Richards, *J. Comp. Chem.* **11**, 159–169 (1990), Semiempirical AM1 electrostatic potential and AM1 electrostatic potential derived charges, a comparison with *ab initio* values.

47. A.K. Rappé and W.A. Goddard III, *J. Phys. Chem.* **95**, 3358–3363 (1991), Charge equilibration for molecular dynamics simulations.

48. C.A. Reynolds, J.W. Essex, and W.G. Richards, *J. Am. Chem. Soc.* **114**, 9075–9079 (1992), Atomic charges for variable molecular conformations.

49. K.B. Wiberg, *J. Am. Chem. Soc.* **87**, 1070–1078 (1965), A scheme for strain energy minimization. Application to the cycloalkanes. (In this paper the first derivatives were calculated numerically, i.e., as finite differences of the energy at two nearly adjacent points differing by a small change in a single Cartesian coordinate.)

50. B.R. Gelin and M. Karplus, *J. Am. Chem. Soc.* **97**, 6996–7006 (1975), Role of structural flexibility in conformational calculations. Application to acetylcholine and *beta*-methylacetylcholine.

51. M. Saunders, K.N. Houk, Y-D. Wu, W.C. Still, M. Lipton, G. Chang, and W.C. Guida, *J. Am. Chem. Soc.* **112**, 1419–1427 (1990), Conformations of cycloheptadecane. A comparison of methods for conformational searching.

52. R.S. Judson, M.E. Colvin, J.C. Meza, A. Huffer, and D. Gutierrez, *Int. J. Quant. Chem.* **44**, 277–290 (1992), Do intelligent configuration search techniques outperform random search for large molecules?

53. J. Li, E. Pratt, B. Weszkowycz, R. Cotterill, and B. Robson, *Biophys. Chem.* **43**, 221–238 (1992), Exploration of the phase space of molecular systems: Assessment of established and new methods.

54. R. Abagyan and P. Argos, *J. Mol. Biol.* **225**, 519–532 (1992), Optimal protocol and trajectory visualization for conformational searches of peptides and proteins.

55. M.E. Tuckerman, G.J. Martyna, and B.J. Berne, *J. Chem. Phys.* **93**, 1287–1291 (1990), Molecular dynamics algorithm for condensed systems with multiple time scales.

56. Because of this, the definition of the internal connectivity of a unit was called the "residue topology file" or RTF [B.R. Gelin, Ph.D. thesis, Harvard University (1976), p. 174]. Even though the units or monomers in nonprotein applications are no longer amino acid residues, the terminology has persisted.

57. J.B. Lagowski and G.J. Vancso, *Int. J. Quant. Chem.* **46**, 271–294 (1993), Polystyrene models. III. Modeling backbone/side-group interactions by an *ab initio* study of 2,4-diphenylpentane.

58. R.A. Sorensen, W.B. Liau, and R.H. Boyd, *Macromolecules* **21**, 194–199 (1988), Prediction of polymer crystal structures and properties. A method using simultaneous *inter-* and *intra-*molecular energy minimization.

59. C. Schmieg and P.C. Hägele, *Colloid. Polym. Sci.* **269**, 449–454 (1991), Atomic calculations of crystal structures of polyisobutylene.

60. P.J. Flory, *Macromolecules* **7**, 381–392 (1974), Foundations of rotational isomeric state theory and general methods for generating configurational averages.

61. J.H.R. Clarke, *Chemistry & Industry*, 780–782 (3 Dec 1990), New opportunities for modelling polymers.

62. B.G. Sumpter, D.W. Noid, and B. Wunderlich, *J. Chem. Phys.* **93**, 6875–6889 (1990), Computer experiments on the internal dynamics of crystalline polyethylene: Mechanistic details of conformational disorder.

63. G.L. Liang, D.W. Noid, B.G. Sumpter, and B. Wunderlich, *Makr. Chem. Theory Simul.* **2**, 245–255 (1993), Dynamics of a paraffin crystal.

64. D.N. Theodorou and U.W. Suter, *Macromolecules* **18**, 1467–1478 (1985), Detailed molecular structure of a vinyl polymer glass.

65. M. Hutnik, F.T. Gentile, P.J. Ludovice, U.W. Suter, and A.S. Argon, *Macromolecules* **24**, 5962–5969 (1991), An atomistic model of the glassy polycarbonate of 4,4′-isopropylidene-diphenol.

66. C.F. Fan and S.L. Hsu, *Macromolecules* **24**, 6244–6249 (1991), Application of the molecular simulation technique to generate the structure of an aromatic polysulfone system.

67. J.I. McKechnie, D. Brown, and J.H.R. Clarke, *Macromolecules* **25**, 1562–1567 (1992), Methods of generating dense relaxed amorphous samples for use in dynamic simulations.

68. G.D. Smith, R.L. Raffe, and D.Y. Yoon, *Macromolecules* **26**, 298–304 (1993), Conformations and order in atactic poly(vinyl chloride) melts from molecular dynamics simulations.

69. R.G. Winkler, P.J. Ludovice, D.Y. Yoon, and H. Morawitz, *J. Chem. Phys.* **95**, 4709–4714 (1991), Computer simulations of *n*-alkane melts.

70. J.A. Darsey, *Macromolecules* **23**, 5274–5278 (1990), Self-consistent field conformational energy study and configurational statistics of poly(dimethylsiloxane).

71. D. Cho, N.A. Neuburger, and W.L. Mattice, *Macromolecules* **25**, 322–326 (1992), Correlations of nearest-neighbor bonds at short times in the internal dynamics of polyisobutylene.

72. A.E. Woodward, *Atlas of Polymer Morphology*, Hanser Publishers, Munich (1989).

73. R. Napolitano, *Makromol. Chemie* **191**, 355–364 (1990), Energy calculations on chain conformation and mode of packing of crystalline isotactic *cis*-1,4-poly(1,3-pentadiene); R. Napolitano, *Makromol. Chemie* **191**, 2435–2466 (1990), Energy calculations on chain conformation and mode of packing of crystalline syndiotactic *cis*-1,4-poly(1,3-pentadiene).

74. R.A. Cageo, A.-I. Schneider, A. Biswas, and J. Blackwell, *Macromolecules* **23**, 2843–2848 (1990), Chain conformation of the Technora copolyamide.

75. K.J. Miller, *Macromolecules* **24**, 6877–6878 (1991), A suggested unit cell for *it*-poly(methyl methacrylate).

76. C. DeRosa, V. Venditto, G. Guerra, B. Pirozzi, and P. Corradini, *Macromolecules* **24**, 5645–5650 (1991), Polymorphism and chain conformations in the crystalline forms of syndiotactic poly(1-butene).

77. R.J. Hobson and A.H. Windle, *Makr. Chem. Theory Simul.* **2**, 257–262 (1993), Diffraction modeling of poly(vinyl chloride): An approach to the crystallinity enigma.

78. V.M. Hallmark, S.P. Bohan, H.L. Strauss, and R.G. Snyder, *Macromolecules* **24**, 4025–4032 (1991), Analysis of the low-frequency isotropic Raman spectrum of molten isotactic polypropylene.

79. N.M. Reynolds and S.L. Hsu, *Macromolecules* **23**, 3463–3472 (1990), A normal vibrational analysis of syndiotactic polystyrene.

80. G.H. Snyder, R. Rowan III, S. Karplus, and B.D. Sykes, *Biochemistry* **14**, 3765–3777 (1975), Complete tyrosine assignments in the high field ^{1}H nuclear magnetic resonance spectrum of the bovine pancreatic trypsin inhibitor.

81. B.R. Gelin and M. Karplus, *Proc. Natl. Acad. USA* **72**, 2002–2006 (1975), Sidechain torsional potentials and motion of amino acids in proteins: bovine pancreatic trypsin inhibitor.

82. M. Hutnik, A.S. Argon, and U.W. Suter, *Macromolecules* **24**, 5970–5979 (1991), Quasi-static modeling of chain dynamics in the amorphous glassy polycarbonate of 4,4'-isopropylidene-diphenol.

83. Y. Zhan and W.L. Mattice, *Macromolecules* **25**, 1554–1561 (1992), Conformation and mobility of 1,4-*trans*-polybutadiene in the crystalline state.

84. D.B. Adolf and M.D. Ediger, *Macromolecules* **25**, 1074–1078 (1992), Cooperativity of local conformational dynamics in simulations of polyisoprene and polyethylene.

85. H. Takeuchi and R.-J. Roe, *J. Chem. Phys.* **94**, 7446–7457 (1991), Molecular dynamics simulation of local chain motion in bulk amorphous polymers. I. Dynamics above the glass transition.

86. M. Doi and S.F. Edwards, *J. Chem. Soc. Faraday Trans. II* **74**, 1789–1801 (1978), Dynamics of concentrated polymer systems. Part 1. Brownian motion in the equilibrium state. *Ibid.*, 1802–1817, Part 2. Molecular motion under flow.

87. D. Rigby and R.-J. Roe, *Macromolecules* **23**, 5312–5319 (1990), Molecular dynamics simulation of polymer liquid and glass. 4. Free-volume distribution.

88. B.G. Sumpter, D.W. Noid, B. Wunderlich, and S.Z.D. Cheng, *Macromolecules* **23**, 4671–4677 (1990), Molecular dynamics study of the rate of melting of a crystalline polyethylene molecule: Effect of chain folding.

89. B.G. Sumpter, D.W. Noid, and B. Wunderlich, *J. Chem. Phys.* **93**, 6875–6889 (1990), Computer experiments on the internal dynamics of crystalline polyethylene: Mechanistic details of conformational disorder.

90. D.W. Noid, B.G. Sumpter, and B. Wunderlich, *Macromolecules* **24**, 4148–4151 (1991), Molecular dynamics simulation of twist motion in polyethylene.

91. B.G. Sumpter, D.W. Noid, and B. Wunderlich, *Macromolecules* **25**, 7247–7255 (1992), Computational experiments on the motion and generation of defects in polymer crystals.

92. H. Takeuchi and R.-J. Roe, *J. Chem. Phys.* **94**, 7458–7465 (1991), Molecular dynamics simulation of local chain motion in bulk amorphous polymers. II. Dynamics at glass transition.

93. C.L. Tucker III, *Fundamentals of Computer Modeling for Polymer Processing*, Hanser Publishers, Munich (1990).
94. S. Enomoto, H. Chuman, and A. Kurihara, *J. Polym. Sci.* **B31**, 77–86 (1993), Elastic modulus and atomic displacements of skeleton and side groups in stretching of a polymer chain.
95. T. Bleha, J. Gajdos, and F.E. Karasz, *Macromolecules* **23**, 4076–4082 (1990), Energetics of strain-induced conformational transitions in polymethylene chains.
96. H. van der Werff, P.T. van Duynen, and A.J. Pennings, *Macromolecules* **23**, 2935–2940 (1990), Deformation energies of chain defects of polyethylene.
97. D.N. Theodorou and U.W. Suter, *Macromolecules* **19**, 139–154 (1986), Atomistic modeling of mechanical properties of polymeric glasses.
98. M. Hutnik, A.S. Argon, and U.W. Suter, *Macromolecules* **26**, 1097–1108 (1993), Simulation of elastic and plastic response in the glassy polycarbonate of 4,4′-isopropylidene-diphenol.
99. D. Brown and J.H.R. Clarke, *Macromolecules* **24**, 2075–2082 (1991), Molecular dynamics simulation of an amorphous polymer under tension 1. Phenomenology.
100. D.N. Theodorou, T.D. Boone, L.R. Dodd, and K.F. Mansfield, *Makr. Chem. Theory Simul.* **2**, 191–238 (1993), Stress tensor in model polymer systems with periodic boundary conditions.
101. G.D. Smith and R.H. Boyd, *Macromolecules* **25**, 1326–1332 (1992), Subglass relaxation. Intermolecular packing and the relaxation times for ester side group reorientation: A molecular dynamics simulation.
102. C.F. Fan and S.L. Hsu, *Macromolecules* **25**, 266–270 (1992), Application of the molecular simulation technique to characterize the structure and properties of an aromatic polysulfone system. 2. Mechanical and thermal properties.
103. J.I. McKechnie, R.N. Haward, D. Brown, and J.H.R. Clarke, *Macromolecules* **26**, 198–202 (1993), Effects of chain configurational properties on the stress–strain behavior of glassy linear polymers.
104. N. Karasawa, S. Dasgupta, and W.A. Goddard III, *J. Phys. Chem.* **95**, 2260–2272 (1991), Mechanical properties and force field parameters for polyethylene crystal.
105. N. Karasawa and W.A. Goddard III, *Macromolecules* **25**, 7268–7281 (1992), Force fields, structures, and properties of poly(vinylidene fluoride) crystals.
106. X. Yang and S.L. Hsu, *Macromolecules* **24**, 6680–6685 (1991), Application of molecular simulation technique to calculate structure and define deformation mechanisms of high-performance polymers.
107. J. Gao and J.H. Weiner, *Macromolecules* **25**, 1348–1356 (1992), Computer simulation of viscoelasticity in polymer melts.
108. D.Y. Yoon, G.D. Smith, and T. Matsuda, *J. Chem. Phys.* **98**, 10037–10043 (1993), A comparison of a united atom and an explicit atom model in simulations of polymethylene.
109. M.J. Grimson, *Molec. Physics* **78**, 7–19 (1993), Fracture of model gel networks under applied strain.
110. W. Zhong, Y. Cai, and D. Tomanek, *Nature* **363**, 435–437 (1 April 1993), Computer simulation of hydrogen embrittlement in metals.
111. P. Meares, *J. Am. Chem. Soc.* **76**, 3415–3422 (1954), The diffusion of gases through polyvinyl acetate.
112. W.W. Brandt, *J. Phys. Chem.* **63**, 1080–1084 (1959), Model calculation of the temperature dependence of small molecule diffusion in high polymers.
113. A.T. DiBenedetto, *J. Polym. Sci.* **A1**, 3477–3487 (1963), Molecular properties of amorphous high polymers. II. An interpretation of gaseous diffusion through polymers.
114. A.T. DiBenedetto and D.R. Paul, *J. Polym. Sci.* **A2**, 1001–1015 (1964), An interpretation of gaseous diffusion through polymers using fluctuation theory.
115. R.J. Pace and A. Daytner, *J. Polym. Sci.* **B17**, 437–451 (1979), Statistical mechanical model for diffusion of simple penetrants in polymers. I. Theory; *ibid.*, pp. 453–464, II. Applications — non-vinyl polymers; *ibid.*, pp. 465–476, III. Applications — vinyl and related polymers.
116. R.J. Pace and A. Daytner, *J. Polym. Sci.* **B17**, 1675–1692 (1979), Statistical mechanical models of diffusion of complex penetrants in polymers. I. Theory; *ibid.*, pp. 1693–1708, II. Applications.
117. B.R. Gelin and M. Karplus, *Proc. Natl. Acad. Sci. USA* **74**, 801–805 (1977), Mechanism of tertiary structural change in hemoglobin; B.R. Gelin, A. W.-M. Lee, and M. Karplus, *J. Mol. Biol.* **171**, 489–559 (1983), Hemoglobin tertiary structural change on ligand binding: Its role in the cooperative mechanism.

118. D.A. Case and M. Karplus, *J. Mol. Biol.* **132**, 343–368 (1979), Dynamics of ligand binding to heme proteins.
119. W. Nowak, R. Czerminski, and R. Elber, *J. Am. Chem. Soc.* **113**, 5627–5637 (1991), Reaction path study of ligand diffusion in proteins: Applications of the self-penalty walk (SPW) method to calculating reaction coordinates for the motion of CO through leghemoglobin.
120. H. Takeuchi and K. Okazaki, *J. Chem. Phys.* **92**, 5643–5652 (1990), Molecular dynamics simulation of diffusion of simple gas molecules in a short chain polymer.
121. H. Takeuchi, *J. Chem. Phys.* **93**, 2062–2067 (1990), A jump motion of small molecules in glassy polymers: A molecular dynamics simulation.
122. H. Takeuchi, R.-J. Roe, and J.E. Mark, *J. Chem. Phys.* **93**, 9042–9048 (1990), Molecular dynamics simulation of diffusion of small molecules in polymers. II. Effects of free volume distribution.
123. F. Müller-Plathe, *J. Chem. Phys.* **94**, 3192–3199 (1991), Diffusion of penetrants in amorphous polymers: A molecular dynamics study.
124. F. Müller-Plathe, *Macromolecules* **24**, 6475–6479 (1991), Calculation of the free energy for gas absorption in amorphous polymers.
125. F. Müller-Plathe, *J. Chem. Phys.* **96**, 3200–3205 (1992), Molecular dynamics simulation of gas transport in amorphous polypropylene.
126. F. Müller-Plathe, S.C. Rogers, and W.F. van Gunsteren, *Macromolecules* **25**, 6722–6724 (1992), Diffusion coefficients of penetrant gases in polyisobutylene can be calculated correctly by molecular dynamics simulations.
127. F. Müller-Plathe, S.C. Rogers, and W.F. van Gunsteren, *J. Chem. Phys.* **98**, 9895–9904 (1993), Gas sorption and transport in polyisobutylene: Equilibrium and nonequilibrium molecular dynamics simulations.
128. R.H. Boyd and P.V. Krishna Pant, *Macromolecules* **24**, 6325–6331 (1991), Molecular packing and diffusion in polyisobutylene.
129. P.V. Krishna Pant and R.H. Boyd, *Macromolecules* **25**, 494–495 (1992), Simulation of diffusion of small-molecule penetrants in polymers.
130. S. Toxvaerd, *J. Chem. Phys.* **93**, 4290–4295 (1990), Molecular dynamics calculation of the equation of state of alkanes.
131. P.V. Krishna Pant and R.H. Boyd, *Macromolecules* **26**, 679–686 (1993), Molecular dynamics simulation of diffusion of small penetrants in polymers.
132. R.M. Sok, H.J.C. Berendsen, and W.F. van Gunsteren, *J. Chem. Phys.* **96**, 4699–4704 (1992), Molecular dynamics simulation of the transport of small molecules across a polymer membrane.
133. C.S. Coughlin, K.A. Mauritz, and R.F. Storey, *Macromolecules* **23**, 3187–3192 (1990), A general free volume based theory for the diffusion of large molecules in amorphous polymers above T_g. 3. Theoretical conformational analysis of molecular shape.
134. D.T. Clark and J.W. Feast, *Polymer Dynamics*, Wiley-Interscience, New York (1978).
135. K.F. Mansfield and D.N. Theodorou, *Macromolecules* **23**, 4430–4445 (1990), Atomistic simulation of a glassy polymer surface.
136. R.F. Saraf, *Macromolecules* **26**, 3623–3620 (1993), Early-stage phase separation in polyimide precursor blends: An atomic force microscopy study.
137. X. Chen, J.A. Gardella, Jr., and P.L. Kumler, *Macromolecules* **26**, 3778–3783 (1992), Surface morphology studies of multiblock and starblock copolymers of poly(α-methylstyrene) and poly-(dimethylsiloxane).
138. K.F. Mansfield and D.N. Theodorou, *Macromolecules* **24**, 4295–4309 (1991), Atomistic simulation of a glassy polymer/graphite interface.
139. W.Y. Shih, W.-H. Shih, and I.A. Aksay, *Macromolecules* **23**, 3291–3296 (1990), Semidilute athermal polymer solutions near a hard wall.
140. J.A. Nieminen, D.B. Abraham, M. Karttunen, and K. Kaski, *Phys. Rev. Lett.* **69**, 124–127 (1992), Molecular dynamics of a microscopic droplet on a solid surface.
141. S.J. Klatte and T.L. Beck, *J. Phys. Chem.* **97**, 5727–5734 (1993), Molecular dynamics of tethered alkanes: Temperature-dependent behavior in a high-density chromatographic system.
142. W. Jilge, I. Carmesin, K. Kremer, and K. Binder, *Macromolecules* **23**, 5001–5013 (1990), A Monte Carlo simulation of polymer–polymer interdiffusion.

143. K. Kremer and G.S. Grest, *J. Chem. Phys.* **92**, 5057–5086 (1990), Dynamics of entangled linear polymer melts: A molecular–dynamics simulation.
144. J.H. Hildebrand and R.L. Scott, *The Solubility of Nonelectrolytes*, 3rd ed., Reinhold Publishing Corporation, NY (1950); reprinted by Dover Publications, New York (1964).
145. P.J. Flory, *J. Chem. Phys.* **10**, 51–61 (1942), Thermodynamics of high polymer solutions; M.L. Huggins, *J. Am. Chem. Soc.* **64**, 1712–1719 (1942), Theory of solutions of high polymers.
146. C.F. Fan, B.D. Olafson, M. Blanco, and S.L. Hsu, *Macromolecules* **25**, 3667–3676 (1992), Application of molecular simulation to derive phase diagrams of binary mixtures.
147. A. Gelb, B.G. Sumpter, and D.W. Noid, *Chem. Phys. Lett.* **169**, 103–108 (1990), Molecular dynamics calculations of energy transfer to polymer surfaces.
148. M.R. Nyden, G.P. Forney, and J.E. Brown, *Macromolecules* **25**, 1658–1666 (1992), Molecular modeling of polymer flammability: Application to the design of flame-resistant polyethylene.
149. E. Blaisten-Barojas and M.R. Nyden, *Chem. Phys. Lett.* **171**, 499–505 (1990), Molecular dynamics study of the depolymerization reaction in simple polymers.
150. M.G. Kanatzidis, *Chem. Eng. News* **68**, 36–54 (3 Dec 1990), Conductive polymers.
151. W. Nie, *Adv. Mater.* **5**, 520–545 (1993), Optical nonlinearity: Phenomena, applications, and materials.
152. See, for example, W.A. Harrison, *Electronic Structure and the Properties of Solids*, W.H. Freeman, San Francisco (1980); J.C. Slater, *Quantum Theory of Molecules and Solids*, McGraw-Hill, New York (1965).
153. R. Hoffmann, C. Janiak, and C. Kollmar, *Macromolecules* **24**, 3725–3746 (1991), A chemical approach to the orbitals of organic polymers.
154. K. Nayak and D.S. Marynick, *Macromolecules* **23**, 2237–2245 (1990), The interplay between geometric and electronic structures in polyisothianaphthene, polyisothianaphthene, polyisonaphthothiophene, polythieno(3,4-b)pyrazine, and polythieno(3,4-b)quinoxaline.
155. J.R. Reynolds, J.P. Ruiz, A.D. Child, K. Nayak, and D.S. Marynick, *Macromolecules* **24**, 678–687 (1991), Electrically conducting polymers containing alternating substituted phenylene and bithiophene repeat units.
156. S.A. Kafafi, J.P. LaFemina, and J.L. Nauss, *J. Am. Chem. Soc.* **112**, 8742–8746 (1990), Electronic structure and conformation of polymers from cluster molecular orbital and molecular mechanics calculations: Polyimide.
157. J.M. Ginder and A.J. Epstein, *Phys. Rev.* **B41**, 10674–10685 (1990), Role of ring torsion in polyaniline: Electronic structure and defect states.
158. J. Corish, V.C.A. Hanratty, D.A. Morton-Blake, F. Beniere, and A. Morin, *J. Mol. Struct. (TheoChem)* **207**, 41–51 (1990), Atomistic simulation calculations on the structures of conducting polymers. Part I. Pristine polyacetylene and polyparaphenylene.
159. J. Corish, V.C.A. Hanratty, J.-P. Margrita, D.A. Morton-Blake, F. Beniere, and A. Morin, *J. Mol. Struct. (TheoChem)* **207**, 53–65 (1990), Atomistic simulation investigations on the structures of conducting polymers. Part II. Doped polyacetylene and polyparaphenylene.
160. D.K. Chakraborty, K.D. Heitzhaus, F.J. Hamilton, H.J. Harwood, and W.L. Mattice, *Macromolecules* **24**, 75–78 (1991), Experimental characterization and molecular modeling of the intramolecular excimer in poly(*p-tert*-butylstyrene).
161. A.R. Tiller, *Macromolecules* **25**, 4605–4611 (1992), Dielectric relaxation in polymers by molecular dynamics simulation.

Index